THE MATRIXIAL HEALING HANDBOOK

INSTANT THERAPY RECIPES

By Paul Chaplin

PREFACE

Matrixial Science is new. It's a comprehensive scientific understanding of how You – all of us – function as a person, and interact with reality: from the material world, to other Selfs.

The detailed science, and the logic which acts as its supporting framework, is set out in my trilogy:

- *Matrixial Logic: Forms of Inequality*
- *Secret Self: Finding the Power of You*
- *The Matrixial Brain: Experiments in Reality*

Over a quarter of a million words, more than 1,500 pages, of explanation and analysis.

This is book about *How To*, not *Why It is*. A book that shows you instant therapy recipes. Whether client or practitioner, you don't need to know why they work.

A GP doesn't need to know the molecular physics of blood flow to diagnose a head cold accurately and prescribe a remedy. Your car mechanic doesn't need to know the electromagnetic field equations of Maxwell to sort your spark plugs.

We're not suggesting that you don't dip into the detailed explanations of Matrixial Science. Just that you don't need to, in order to enjoy its practical benefits.

For those who do want to explore, we'd recommend starting with Part 2 *Healing How*. Or you can just use and enjoy the Recipes in Part 1 without ever setting foot in Part 2. For the next step in further reading, I'd suggest exploring *The Matrixial Brain*. This is a curation of Experiments, with explanations of theory relevant to them. The immediate upside of these Experiments, is that you can do them at home. You too can then see how your own experiences of doing these Experiments compares the test groups: dozens of randomly selected volunteers from around the UK. You can be your own witness to how Matrixial Science techniques can alter your reality: mental, emotional and physical.

You need no special skills, background or knowledge to work through the Recipes. Perhaps some patience and a willingness to think new things. Please bring lots of scepticism. That's intellectually healthy. Start from the proposition that a Recipe can't possibly work. That's it's all hocus pocus. Then: see what happens in your own experience.

You can go through the Recipes in the order presented, or dip in as the subject matter interests you. The *Explaining* notes are deliberately non-technical. They're written to give you a general idea of what's going on and why it's working.

Some of the Recipes have half a dozen steps. Some have

multiple Parts of Steps. This can be very challenging to work through, reading as you go, or trying to remember all the steps. So I've created the **Matrixial Audio Recipes**. You can simply play the Recipe you're interested in. Sit back, close your eyes and follow the Steps.

The timing of the Steps is important. That's why the Steps include pacing lines. Ones that go: *Relax*; *Close your eyes*; and so on. It looks a bit repetitive on the page. But you can *feel* how the pacing works when you work with the **Matrixial Audio Recipes**.

Many of the Recipes use a technique which involves imagining a "second you": *You2*. This *You2* is just You. Not a younger self or a future self. It's not that sort of imagination. It's just thinking of a "second you".

This might appear novel and challenging. It really isn't. This is something that you do, all day long, without even thinking about it. We just get you to put this *You2* at the "front" of your mind, for a while. I've never met a client or friend who finds any difficulty doing *You2* stuff. Most of us had an invisible friend when we were pre-school age. The act of visualisation is that easy.

If there's some mental barrier which makes the visualisation not so easy, then: *just imagine that you can visualise You2*. Then, just like that, you can.

8

This is not a book about how you can "become a better You" through practice. You were born perfect: with systems operating under an architecture. That got you through the toughest time of your life: from birth to 7 years old. You can obtain benefits instantly from all the Recipes in this book. There's no practice needed. No slogging up the slopes of a distant mountain towards betterment.

If you're looking for a book of daily meditations, mantras or acknowledgements, or a guide to daily journaling of whatever upsets you. Or lengthy dialogues with your "troubled inner self" - a book of how to talk to yourself, with rebukes or affirmations. That's not this book.

If you want instant cures for mental, emotional and physical issues: that's this book. Remedies you can use in minutes. Results you can experience in reality. Here and now.

For problems that we actually cause in our Selfs, repeatedly, use of the relevant Recipe can be repeated, as You feel the need. For other problems, for example a sports injury, once the Recipe has been used to cure you: you don't need to come back.

Now it's over to you and your life.

Paul Chaplin
2021

THE MATRIXIAL THERAPY PRACTICE

If you would like access to a Matrixial Therapy Practitioner, please go to the Therapy Practice website.

https://www.matrixial-healing.com/

Our *Healing* Recipes aren't limited to what you'll read in the book. If you have a problem, please contact us through the website. We enjoy exploring new challenges: that's how *Matrixial Therapy* grows.

THE AUDIO RECIPES

Follow and experience the Recipes, with your eyes closed.

Find the **Matrixial Audio Recipes** at:
www.matrixial-recipes.com

PART (1)
HEALING NOW

CHAPTER 1

ANXIETY ISSUES

In this Section, we look at Anxiety Issues.

In popular culture and in psychotherapy, Anxiety is much misunderstood. It's viewed as a problem, and a source of problems. It isn't.

Anxiety is born into all of us, as a necessary part of our *Anxiety-Soothing Rhythm* ("ASR"). The amazing natural process which kept us alive as babies, and keeps our lives on track. In Part 2 *Healing How*, there's further explanation of how all this works.

We create Anxiety issues. By interfering with our ASR, and in particular, by repressing our Anxiety function. We repress Anxiety, because we feel it as unpleasant and we worry that we can't cope with letting the Anxiety flow.

That repression grants us a certain kind of energy, and an illusion of power. It's the same dynamic as other types of self-harming.

The energy is toxic and short-lived. To keep generating the energy, we need more and more input. This constant struggling against what is a natural ASR tires us out. As we tire, we become less able to engage Anxiety repression strategies.

That increases our delusional fear of Anxiety, because we come to feel that we can't control it.

We can't think our way out of Anxiety. But we don't need to. What our *Anxiety-Soothing Rhythm* needs is to be left alone, or even better, encouraged.

You don't stuff a pillow over a baby's face when it cries. That crying is the natural acting out of baby Anxiety. It's what gets attention from the carer, who supplies the baby's needs. And so generates the Soothing part of the ASR.

That's what we need to do with Anxiety issues. To help the Client with stopping the interference with themselves, which is actually causing the problems mistakenly associated with Anxiety.

We want to help the Client to enjoy Anxiety as a life-lighting energy source. An inexhaustible energy supply that is gifted to us at birth, and which we can simply allow to act as the electricity supply for all that we want to achieve in life.

1.   *Instant Anxiety Relief*

Scenario

Client presents with self-report of Anxiety issues.

Typical reporting:
- I feel anxious all the time
- I feel anxious and it stops me going out [or otherwise enjoying life normally]
- I wake up anxious
- I get anxious around sleeping
- I just feel something bad is going to happen

Here, we are dealing with generalised Anxiety, where there's no obvious single cause.

Say you're going for a job interview. It's natural to feel Anxiety. That Anxiety is conditioning you to be ready to act out. Your Soothing will kick in when it's appropriate: if you just let it.

You can use the Instant Meditation Recipe below, if you want a quick re-balancing before doing something specific which is naturally and appropriately Anxiety inducing.

Healing

Step 1
1.   Find some alone space.
2.   Sit down anywhere comfortable.

3.   Take the top two fingers of whatever is your
        writing hand.
4.   Place those fingers gently on the waist side of
        your tummy. (You can find the location simply
        by placing your two fingers over your belly
        button, then moving them around to your writing
        hand side).
5.   Rest your fingers at that spot.
6.   Close your eyes.
7.   Breathe normally.

Step 2
1.   Take the top two fingers of your other hand.
2.   Place them gently at the back of your neck, on the
        other side of your body from your other fingers.
        (Location is anywhere between the nape of your
        neck and your collar-bone: just gently move your
        fingers till you find a spot that feels fine to you).
3.   Breathe normally.

Step 3: Take 1 to 2 Minutes
1.   Feel a connection between your fingers.
2.   A connection running through your upper body.
        Like a wire.
3.   You may feel it hot. You may feel it cold.
4.   If it's a hot connection, allow it to get hotter.
        If it's a cold connection, allow it to get colder.
5.   Allow the connection to become more intense.
6.   Feel it like the filament in a light bulb, getting

brighter as you turn up the voltage.

7.   Allow yourself to allow those toxic energy feelings to run through that connection.

8.   Between your fingers, it feels like angry electric ants scurrying around.

9.   It feels like the connection is becoming barbed wire, spilling toxic chemicals into your body.

10.   Let the angry energy become more intense.

11.   And more. Filling your chest and your head.

Step 4

1.   Now it's coursing through you. That toxic writhing energy.

2.   Take the hand with the fingers which are at your waist.

3.   Take the palm of that hand.

4.   Place it gently over the centre of your chest.

5.   Still feel the angry toxic energy coursing through you.

Step 5

1.   Now, you're going in a few moments to take a huge breath in.

2.   Through your nose or your mouth.

3.   However you'd do it if you were about to jump into a swimming pool.

4.   Big breath in: *Now*.

5.   Hold that breath for 3 long seconds.

6.   One … Two … Three…

7.   Let it out, and at the same time, press your palm into your chest.
8.   You can fall back into your chair, or into a lying position, if you like.
9.   Rest. Breathe normally.
10.   Think whatever thoughts you think. Feel whatever feelings you feel.

End.

Explaining
This is applied *Biomorphics*.

When we created that sense of connection between your fingers, we stimulated your Anxiety generation system. We got you to feel what you well recognise as intense Anxiety.

Well, you don't quite recognise it, because you spend so much time suppressing it. You have created a delusional fear that, if you allow yourself to feel that Anxiety, you can't control it.

You're right. We can't control Anxiety with our conscious mind. We don't need to. Nature created a perfect *Anxiety-Soothing Rhythm* for us. When we feel Anxiety, a matching amount of Soothing always comes to greet it: to extinguish the fire.

So, we got you to experience intense, searing Anxiety. Then, with the breath interruption Step, we got your conscious mind to leave the room. We stopped you from trying to stop the Anxiety.

If you review the history of your head during the 3-second breath interruption Step, you'll notice that your head became empty. You had no word-based thoughts. Just an emptiness.

As you breathed out, the Anxiety just disappeared. You felt hit by a massive wave of Soothing. We have you press the palm into your chest to signal to your mind and body that the Anxiety episode is over.

You now feel utterly restful and peaceful. More than that. You have feelings of:
• Balance
• Power
• Control
• Energy

These are unusual feelings for you. The exact opposite to your generalised Anxiety state. It feels great. It feels... You.

That's exactly what you are feeling. The power and balance that was inside You all the time. It was only your attempts to think your way into interfering with the

ASR which was causing the problems with Anxiety you reported.

Now you have experienced the feeling of power which comes from that natural balance. Allowing the ASR to do what it is always capable of doing.

After Care
You can experience this balance, peace and power: anytime.

Now you have felt, for the first time since you were a small child, the unimpeded working of your ASR. That experience, just on its own, will now stop you getting those anti-Anxiety feelings at that awful level which was disrupting your life.

If you never repeat this Recipe, the experience you have just had will lower your anti-Anxiety toxicity for a long time. You can struggle to re-toxify yourself, if you really want to. This helps you to realise that it's you deliberately choosing to re-toxify you: not something happening in you which you can't control.

Now you can begin to get used to the idea that when you are re-experiencing those toxic feelings, it's not Anxiety that you are feeling: it is your own mind-body system fighting off your attempts to repress natural anxiety.

You have experienced that place, where Anxiety peaks, and Soothing kicks in. You've experienced the balance, peace and power this brings to you: instantly.

So, you can do this exercise whenever you like. Even when you're not suffering from anti-Anxiety repression.

As you practice the routine, you'll find, just after a few goes, that you can simply think the *Instant Anxiety Relief*. You just think about your fingers going where they do in the exercise; the angry electric ants; the head space emptying as you hold breath; and the matching of Soothing as you breathe out.

The simple repetition of the Recipe creates a pattern in a distinct part of your brain. It's like a piece of music, ready to play at the touch of a button. You just think of the Recipe, and that presses the "play" button.

Your mind-body responds just as if you had actually done the Recipe. It's great sometimes actually to perform the Recipe.

Why would you not want to feel balance, peace and power: anytime? Instantly.

2. Panic Attack Intervention

You can't easily do this one on your own.
You really need a Practitioner to help you at Step 8.

Scenario

Client presents with self-report of suffering panic attacks. It's even better when Client is suffering a present attack in the presence of the Practitioner.

Typical reporting:

- My heart is pounding
- I feel like I can't breathe
- I feel terrified
- I've had this in the middle of the night and had to call an ambulance

Healing

Step 1

1.   Find some alone space.
2.   Sit down anywhere comfortable.
3.   Allow yourself to feel as jittery as you often do.

Step 2

1.   Take the palm of your writing hand.
2.   Place it over your tummy: just where your tummy button is.
3.   Make sure to leave a little gap between your palm and your tummy. This is really important. The gap should be a finger-width.
4.   Close your eyes now.
5.   Focus on breathing in through the palm of your hand.
6.   Feel yourself drawing in breaths, through the

palm of your hand.

7.   Remember how when you were inside your mummy, that's where your life support came into your body.

8.   You can breathe deep or shallow. Slow or fast. Whatever works.

Step 3

1.   Your eyes are still closed.

2.   Take the palm of your other hand.

3.   Place it over your chest.

4.   Make sure to leave a little gap between your palm and your chest. This is really important. The gap should be a finger-width.

5.   Focus on breathing out through the palm of your hand.

6.   Feel yourself pushing out breaths, through the palm of your hand.

You may feel some resistance to this breathing. That's normal and fine.

We call Steps 2 and 3 *Angel Wings*.

Step 4

1.   Your eyes are still closed.

2.   Rest both your hands.

3.   Take the top two fingers of whatever is your writing hand and hover them just above the centre of your chest.

4.   Breathe in, as deep as you can.
5.   Hold it for 3 seconds.
6.   Tap those fingers on your chest twice: Tap …
        Tap.

Step 5
1.   Do Step 4 another 2 times.

Step 6
1.   Repeat Steps 2 and 3 *Angel Wings*.

This time, you will feel much less resistance to the breathing.

Step 7
1.   Take the top two fingers of whatever is your
        writing hand.
2.   Place them at the side of your tummy.
3.   Make sure to leave a little gap between your
        fingers and your body. This is really important.
        The gap should be a finger-width.
4.   Now just focus on that gap.
5.   You will start to feel a tingling, an itching.
6.   Let that itching intensify.
7.   Allow the sensations it triggers to run through
        your chest.
8.   It's really unpleasant.
9.   Those toxic feelings will start to flood through
        you.

10.   All the way into your chest and up to your throat.
11.   Into your head. Making your head buzz.
12.   Making you feel toxic and dizzy and sick: like you're having a panic attack.

Step 8

This Step is where a Practitioner is better used.

1.   The Practitioner will distract you.
2.   With talk about anything: ideally silly and non-consequential.
3.   30 seconds to one minute of distraction.

If you are doing this Recipe alone, then:

4.   Stop what you're doing at Step 7.
5.   Distract yourself for 30 seconds to one minute: walk around, switch on the TV; anything.

Step 9

1.   Repeat Steps 2 and 3 *Angel Wings*.

This time, you will feel little or no resistance to the breathing.

Stop when you feel like you want to.

End.

Explaining

You're not suffering Panic, nor are you being Attacked.

This is a problem which has built up from constant Anxiety repression. You've been really successful in repressing your Anxiety. So much so that your Soothing response has gone to sleep.

Your Soothing only responds to Anxiety. So it needs that Anxiety to flow in the first place. But you've become really skilled at halting your Anxiety flow at the first sign of it.

To achieve this, you've been putting yourself in the place you would be if under outside attack: like a soldier sheltering from incoming shells and bullets. That's *Stress*. Under Stress, you shut down Anxiety, because the last thing you want is to be Soothed. It's not survivally smart to be wandering around a battlefield, feeling calm, balance and peace.

So Stress prevents Soothing, by stopping Anxiety flowing in the first place. That's what you're doing to yourself. That's why it feels like an "Attack".

This Recipe is more applied *Biomorphics*.

First of all, we interrupt your interruption: Steps 2 and 3 *Angel Wings*. We disrupt your Anxiety repression, by creating a null space inside you. Although you don't know and can't realise, your *Anxiety-Soothing Rhythm* is still operating: just at a low level.

So, in this first step, we are promoting the ASR dynamic. Attuning your system to it. Getting your over-active thinking out of the way, a little.

Your mind resists. It's craving the *Stress*. So we let your mind have what it wants. With Steps 4 and 5, we give you a super, maxi-Stress experience. But this time, we're taking your feet off the accelerator and the brake. We are encouraging those feelings of Stress to run riot, all the way through you.

But, the natural balancing systems you were born with are way smarter than anything you can think. Your entire Self looks around and says: "I'm not on a battlefield, or being chased by a sabre-toothed tiger or a serial killer. I'm sitting in my sofa at home."

Your Self's innate systems analyse where you are and what's going on around you. They feel what's happening inside you: stimulated by the two fingers connection.

Your systems recognise that angry, buzzing, toxic set of sensations as: Anxiety.

So, now you've triggered genuine, ordinary, helpful Anxiety. Now we need to distract you, so that you don't interrupt the ASR: as you have become so skilled in doing. We tell you a silly story, we push a custard pie in our faces. Whatever's silly and distracting.

In those moments, your Soothing wave rises and quenches the Anxiety fire. Automatically. No need for your thinking mind to get its boots on.

Now, we seal the deal with a replay of Steps 2 and 3 *Angel Wings*. This time, you can't use fake Stress to get out of the ASR. You can't resist.

And you gently, over those tens of seconds with *Angel Wings*, come to feel that you want to stay right there.

Now, you are really feeling: balance, peace and power. Exactly those things which you feared you couldn't feel. Which caused you to invent *Stress*-scapes to repress Anxiety.

Here's something you're not now feeling: control. You don't control a perfect summer's day, a blissful orgasm, the taste of your favourite food. You *experience* it.

You've been using Panic Attacks, upon yourself, as an instrument of control. One that never works, however much you ratchet up the pseudo-pain.

Now, you're feeling balance, peace and power: without

feeling the need for control. Now, you're not down in the lowest depths, you're floating free over the mountain tops.

After Care
You can experience this balance, peace and power: anytime.

Now you have felt the unimpeded working of your ASR. That experience, just on its own, will now stop you getting those anti-Anxiety feelings at that awful level which was disrupting your life.

If you never repeat this Recipe, the experience you have just had will lower your anti-Anxiety toxicity for a long time. Your ability to mount Panic Attacks on yourself has now been seriously reduced.

Go on: try it right now, and see what happens:
have a Panic Attack practice

You see? It's just not happening. It's like you can't find the panic button.

You can struggle to re-toxify yourself, if you really want to. This helps you to realise that it's you deliberately choosing to re-toxify you: not something happening in you which you can't control.

Now you can begin to get used to the idea that when you are re-experiencing those toxic feelings, it's not Panic that you are feeling. It's you faking Stress reactions just to repress your natural born gift of Anxiety.

You have now experienced that place, where Anxiety peaks, and Soothing kicks in. You've experienced the balance, peace and power this brings to you: instantly.

So, you can do this exercise whenever you like. Even when you're not suffering from fake Stress syndrome.

As you practice the routine, you'll find, just after a few goes, that you can simply think the *Panic Attack Intervention*. Just rattle through the Steps in your head.

The simple repetition of the Recipe creates a pattern in a distinct part of your brain. It's like a piece of music, ready to play at the touch of a button. You just think of the Recipe, and that presses the "play" button.

Then, if you feel like you want to have a Panic Attack, your mind-body responds just as if you had actually done the Recipe.

As you've already experienced, with a *Panic Attack practice*: there's now something which is actually stopping you going there. The harder you try to Panic, the more strongly the Recipe will engage.

Balance, peace and power: anytime. Instantly. Panic doesn't get to attack anymore.

3.   *Instant Meditation*

Scenario

Meditation is a nuisance. People go to all sorts of lengths to try and achieve meditative states. From investing in Lycra leggings and whale music to trekking up Himalayan mountains to consort with a culture of odd life experiences.

There are loads of illegal drugs that can get you to much the same place. Although the significant health risks associated with their ingestion mean you're best not trying them.

What, exactly, is meditation supposed to be about? Some meditative states are about holding an empty mind. Others are about "mindful awareness": you just allow thoughts to pass before you, without judgment.

As readers of my book *Secret Self* will be aware, this "mindfulness" is nonsensical. Reflecting upon our thoughts, via the mirrors architecturally plumbed into our subjective mind, is exactly how we think, every moment.

This "mindful awareness" is nothing other than a

deliberate attempt to create a fake mirror. It's not how our minds are designed to work, and that's why it's so hard to achieve. It's like trying to breathe out by breathing in: that's not the way our lungs are designed by nature.

There are lots of ways of adjusting our thinking, but they all come down to two routes:

- Top-down *Psychotectics*: from our objective mind (what we call Theta Θ), operating through electromagnetic fields arising from the energy functions of our cells;
- Bottom-up *Biomorphics*: from the systems of our physical body, which provide information to our subjective mind.

The other way, is playing around within the bounded infinity of our subjective mind. This is the playground of classical meditation techniques. It's just swapping one set of arbitrary made-up subjective thoughts with another.

There's nothing wrong with doing that, any more than there's anything wrong with rearranging the clothes in your wardrobe. But it doesn't change those clothes, or make them cleaner or better.

When a person wants to experience "mindful awareness", what they actually seek is an experience of feeling: balance, peace and power. We can get you there.

But first we need to empty your head.

Healing
Step 1
1.   Find some alone space.
2.   Sit down anywhere comfortable.
3.   Allow yourself to feel as jittery as you often do.

Step 2
1.   Take the palm of your writing hand.
2.   Place it over your tummy: just where your tum
        my button is.
3.   Make sure to leave a little gap between your
        palm and your tummy. This is really important.
        The gap should be a finger-width.
4.   Close your eyes now.
5.   Focus on breathing in through the palm of your
        hand.
6.   Feel yourself drawing in breaths, through the
        palm of your hand.
7.   Remember how when you were inside your
        mummy, that's where your life support
        came into your body.
8.   You can breathe deep or shallow. Slow or fast.
        Whatever works.

Step 3
1.   Your eyes are still closed.
2.   Take the palm of your other hand.

3.   Place it over your chest.
4.   Make sure to leave a little gap between your
        palm and your chest. This is really important.
        The gap should be a finger-width.
5.   Focus on breathing out through the palm of
        your hand.
6.   Feel yourself pushing out breaths, through the
        palm of your hand.

You may feel some resistance to this breathing. That's
normal and fine.

We call Steps 2 and 3 *Angel Wings*.

Step 4

1.   Your eyes are still closed.
2.   Now, focus on allowing the breathing energy
        you draw in, to divide: part going down
        your body to your toes; part going up to the top
        of your head.
3.   Just allow that breath energy to flow as it will.

Step 5

1.   Now allow the energy which you breathe out
        through the palm of your hand, to come
        back into you; as you're breathing in through the
        palm of your lower hand.
2.   Still allow the energy you're breathing in
        through the palm of your lower hand, to divide:

> part going down your body to your toes;
> part going up to the top of your head

Carry on, as long as you like.

End.

Explaining

Steps 2 and 3 *Angel Wings*, "empty" your head. If you review the history of your head, you'll see that during this time, your head was empty. It's like your mind being represented by dancers on a crowded dance floor. The music stops, and the dancers – your thoughts - move to the sides of your head, leaving a silent, empty space.

Step 4 is diffusion. This will sound quite science-y, but we're allowing the electromagnetic ("EM") fields of all the cells in your body, to interact, with minimal interruption from your thoughts.

Step 5 is matching. You're matching the valance of the EM fields arising from your cells, with the valence of your aggregate "whole body" EM field.

The meditative effect is achieved by making narrow-banded <coherence> in your /S/ domain.

In plain English, we are not exactly "emptying" your subjective mind. We are getting the thoughts within it to line up with each other, in balance with each other, and in a narrow corridor. We are creating static order out of dynamic order.

This prevents you from "seeing" your thoughts. That's why your head feels empty.

This is only temporary, and is meant to be so. Imagine being stuck in the same ordering of thoughts forever. You'd go mad very quickly.

Our minds are designed so that our thoughts swirl around gravitation centres: what we call the 5 Slices (Needs/ Wants; Chemistry; Empathy; Challenge; Security) . It's that movement which is our personality. It's through that movement that we learn. You can read more about this in Part 2 *Healing How*.

So far as "mindful awareness" is anything other than unscientific nonsense, it's an attempt to stop gravity. Or as advocates like to imagine, creating some viewing gallery outside the universe of your own mind, so you can watch what's going on.

Well, you can't escape the universe of your own mind. It's all you have. Trying to do that results in what we call Ш Shadow Slices. That is something we try and do all the time. Trying to get a handle, or an angle, on our thoughts. We spend a lot of time in Matrixial Therapy actually curing the unfortunate results of over-investment in Ш Shadow Slices.

And there's a community out there trying energetically, in Lycra, with whale and rain music, to get you to manufacture more Ш Shadow Slices.

You're the Boss of you. If you want to mildly (and potentially seriously) mentally self-harm in this way, then that's your call. Or, you can just throw away the viewing platforms which you have already created, without meditative assistance. Throw them away for a few moments. Then you get to create new ones, which always give you a new perspective.

After Care
You can repeat *Instant Meditation* whenever you want to.

As you do repetitions, it will become easier to just press the "button" in your mind (your objective Θ field), and experience some of the "real thing".

But, take a minute or three. Get the energy flowing between your palm gaps and you. Allow the energy fields of all the cells in your body to communicate with each other, with minimal interference from your subjective mind.

Take an *Instant Meditation* break and come back to the same you, but different.

4.   *Phobias*

In *I Want To Love But… Feeling the Power of You*,[1] Chapter 3, we wrote:

> Clinically, and in common sense, we separate Fear Dynamics into 2 types:
> - Fears in Reality
> - Phobias
>
> The difference between these is that: Fears in Reality are about events that can cause actual pain. That pain can be physical (breaking your leg); or mental (breaking your heart). There is huge overlap and linkage between the mental and physical, of course.
>
> Phobias are concerns that have reality only in your imagination: you are never going to die from walking on cracks in the pavement; or being close to a house spider.
>
> Alongside phobias are Superstitions: phobias that a community of people have come to share, and pass down the generations as "folk wisdom", or these days "urban myths".
>
> It's an interesting psychological phenomenon, that we can laugh at a particular superstition (Friday

---

[1] the Author (2019)

13[th)], yet be fully invested in our reality of a phobia (house spiders). This is an example of "cognitive dissonance".

That's the absolutely important difference between the Fears Dynamic and the Anxieties Dynamic:

- we are born with an Anxieties Dynamic, and it is the key driver for our growth;
- we are not born with a Fears Dynamic; we learn it in later life.

Your Anxieties Dynamic is, literally, written into the DNA of You, from the moment of birth. The toddler doesn't have a Fears Dynamic. That is only capable of being acquired as the child brain grows and starts operating in adult brain-waves (Gamma, Beta). By 7YO, a child will have acquired parts of a Fears Dynamic.

These can be quite powerful. I remember I was chased up the garden and bowled over by an enthusiastic Alsatian. Must have been around school starting age for Tiny Ted. Then, a few years back, I went to Crufts dog show at Earls Court with a canine enthusiast companion. There was a kind of mini-pound with a few Alsatians pawing around in it. Meaning no harm, they went all barky, running up to the (pretty thin) pound wiring. I yelped and jumped out of my skin. Good thing my persona isn't tough guy about town, or that date would have been ruined. As it was, my companion settled me down and helped wipe the spilt coffee off my chinos.

Your Fears Dynamic is an ever changing set of decorations on You-Tree: in size, shape, colour and which branch they are attached to from time to time and place to place.

This leads us to another very important principle: *Anxiety is never wrong. Feeling fear can be a mistake.*

So can *feeling Glad* of or for something. We are very often mistaken in feeling glad about buying that dress, which turns out to be a disaster. Or supporting that team which just lost again at home.

Yet, if I suggested that you shouldn't feel glad of shopping, or ice cream: you'd tell me not to be so silly and mind your own business. We all feel completely comfortable that we can choose and change the things we feel Glad of, without any outside help: thank you very much.

Question for You to think about for later: Why do we believe that feeling Fear works differently from feeling Glad?

This book urges You, not to change You, but to become a bigger You: to grow.

So, what does that mean for us in this book? We'll take that definition of "Phobia": a fear that isn't rooted in any reality of your life circumstances.

Let's get rid of one, by example.

Scenario
The Client self-reports being afraid of spiders. Even little ones.

Healing

PART 1 FEAR

Step 1

1.   Sit down for this one.
2.   You'll need a bit of paper or post it note; and a pen.
3.   Hold up the paper.
4.   Write in 1 word, or draw a picture of your Fear.
5.   Look at it. Make sure that you feel what that word or picture means to you.
6.   Pop yourself up, put the paper under you, and sit down on it.

End.

PART 2 ANXIETY

Step 1

1.   Find some alone space.
2.   Sit down anywhere comfortable.
3.   Take the top two fingers of whatever is your writing hand.
4.   Place those fingers gently on the waist side of your tummy. (You can find the location sim ply by placing your two fingers over your belly button, then moving them around to your writing hand side).
5.   Rest your fingers at that spot.
6.   Close your eyes.
7.   Breathe normally.

Step 2

1.   Take the top two fingers of your other hand.
2.   Place them gently at the back of your neck, on the other side of your body from your other fingers. (Location is anywhere between the nape of your neck and your collar-bone: just gently move your fingers till you find a spot that feels fine to you).
3.   Breathe normally.

Step 3: Take 1 to 2 Minutes

1.   Feel a connection between your fingers.
2.   A connection running through your upper body. Like a wire.

3.   You may feel it hot. You may feel it cold.

4.   If it's a hot connection, allow it to get hotter. If it's a cold connection, allow it to get colder.

5.   Allow the connection to become more intense.

6.   Feel it like the filament in a light bulb, getting brighter as you turn up the voltage.

7.   Allow yourself to allow those toxic energy feelings to run through that connection.

8.   Between your fingers, it feels like angry electric ants scurrying around.

9.   It feels like the connection is becoming barbed wire, spilling toxic chemicals into your body.

10.   Let the angry energy become more intense.

11.   And more. Filling your chest and your head.

Step 4

1.   Now it's coursing through you. That toxic writhing energy.

2.   Take the hand with the fingers which are at your waist.

3.   Take the palm of that hand.

4.   Place it gently over the centre of your chest.

5.   Still feel the angry toxic energy coursing through you.

Step 5

1.   Now, you're going in a few moments to take a huge breath in.

2.   Through your nose or your mouth.

3.   However you'd do it if you were about to jump into a swimming pool.

4.   Big breath in: *Now*.

5.   Hold that breath for 3 long seconds.

6.   One … Two … Three…

7.   Let it out, and at the same time, press your palm into your chest.

8.   You can fall back into your chair, or into a lying position, if you like.

9.   Rest. Breathe normally.

10.   Think whatever thoughts you think. Feel what ever feelings you feel.

End.

PART 3 VANISHING

Step 1

1.   Pop yourself up and retrieve that piece of paper.

2.   Look at your word or picture.

3.   Go find the feelings you used to associate with it.

4.   Ok: you can't feel anything there.

Step 2

1.   Close your eyes.

2.   See the word or picture in your head.

3.   Go find the feelings you used to associate with it.

4.   Ok: you can't feel anything there.

5.   Open your eyes.

6.   Breathe.

7.   Say "Bye Bye!"

End.

Explaining

The simple explanation is that we used Anxiety to burn away the "fake" Fear. Then allowed Soothing to pour water on the ashes.

To keep that Fear going, you have to invest energy. It takes a lot of energy to keep an illusion going. You borrow that energy by repressing your Anxiety. But you pay for that loan in the form of loss of control. That's why the Fear feels uncontrollable. You're using oil to put out a chip pan fire that you started.

After Care

The Client sees immediate relief from this *Healing*. But the real test is next time the Client actually confronts that Fear experience in the real world. By practicing the Technique Steps, the Client can create a "go to" button in themselves. It's actually a pattern in their "computer" brain.

In response to that Fear stimulus, the button gets pushed, the ASR works its magic, and the afraid becomes fearless.

CHAPTER 2

SLEEP DISORDERS

In this Part, we're going to look at issues with:
- getting to sleep
- being in sleep
- coming awake

In sleep, we are disconnected from the usual ways that we connect with the world. This allows us to enjoy amazing experiences. The flipside is that it can burden us with terrible problems.

Technical Explanation (feel free to pass over)
Drawing on analysis in *Secret Self,* all these issues take place in a context that is much misunderstood in popular culture and psychology. Matrixial Science tells us that:
> *dreaming is /S/ubjective {identation}[2] out of | T | ime.*

The excision of temporal order in the sleep state results in our usual direction being obverted. In waking awareness:
- our | E | motion points forwards in | T | ime: the headlights
- our /S/ubjective thinking points backwards in | T | ime: the rear-view mirror.

---

[2] "identation" is a word coined by Matrixial science, to describe the process by which certain types of things are created in our heads. Things we use words like "thoughts", "ideas" and "feelings" to describe.

45

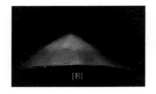

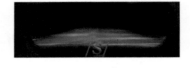

This temporal direction depends upon | congruence |, which is founded upon our becoming in perpetual relationship with the world | W |.

In the sleep state, the Architectural structure of our Self | congruence | remains, but it is unaffixed to physio-temporal interaction with the | W | orld and thus, in response to | W |. Our | congruence | architecture floats free of the world which creates and sustains it.

Thus our {identation} becomes, simply, confused. The reality checks which we, in waking awareness, rely upon for <coherence>, are temporarily lost.

Our | E | headlights can become turned back on dream-figments of ourselves. We figment parallel dimensions out of / S / {idents}, which our waking <coherence> would not allow.

The gravity of the Slices still has effect, which is why we dream within limits which we can discern upon reconstructing our dreams. The Slices don't have the gravitational power of our waking state, because they are

not being "fed" by all the stimuli usually available from
I W I => I P I hysiology interactions.

All this has profound consequences for dream analysis.
And for therapeutic interventions directed towards
allowing you to re-integrate dream experiences in your
waking manifest.

Plain English Explanation
In plainer English, when we're awake we are connected
in time to our own body and to the outside world. When
we're asleep, that connection with the outside world is
not completely lost: but greatly restricted. That's a natural
biological function. Our brains stop us being disturbed by
what's going on outside our bodies: that's how the sleep
state is able to continue for sleeping hours.

It's the disconnecting of that link in time – with the
outside world – that allows the dreamscape. We create
nightmares out of two types of anti-time:
- trying to use our emotions to look at the past
  (instead of the future)
- trying to use our thoughts to look at the future
  (instead of the past).

Once we understand these dynamics, it's easy to adjust
dreaming patterns, so that we don't have these nightmares.
Knowing that we're not going to have them, or that we can
control them if we want to, takes away our fear of sleep.

After all nobody who is confident that sleep will be a nice place to be, gets worried about going to sleep.

Waking can be weird. In good and bad ways. We'll give you a *Healing* which allows you to have confidence that you can experience awakening as a positive experience for you: without you having to bother thinking any thoughts about it.

So now: let's get to sleep.

5.   Sleep Induction Techniques

Scenario
Client typically presents with this self-reporting:
- I have trouble getting to sleep
- I can just lie there tossing and turning for hours
- I do get to sleep, but then keep waking up
- My sleep troubles get me anxious around going to sleep.

Now the first, non-Matrixial remedy for this is simply to alter your sleep patterns. There's a wonderful book all about this by Matthew Walker: *Why We Sleep*.[3] It's full of fascinating information about how sleep works, without technical science jargon.

---

[3] HTTPS://WWW.AMAZON.CO.UK/DP/B06Y649387/REF=DP-KINDLE-REDIRECT?_
ENCODING=UTF8&BTKR=1

Have a go at sleeping for anything from 30 minutes to 90 minutes *during the day*. Ideally, late afternoon. This won't cure your night-time sleep issues. But it will at least mean that you're getting some good quality sleep at some point in the 24 hour cycle.

Having a refreshing afternoon nap can also help you, at a basic level, to lower your distress issues around night time sleep.

5A   Healing for Sleep

Step 1

1.   Find some alone space.
2.   Sit down anywhere comfortable.
3.   You need to be in a position where you can fall back, when the Steps require. So please be on the edge of a sofa, the edge of your bed, or just sitting on the floor.
4.   Think about sleep and you.
5.   Allow yourself to feel distress around your sleeping, as you often do.

Step 2

1.   Take the palm of your writing hand.
2.   Place it over your tummy: just where your tum my button is.
3.   Make sure to leave a little gap between your palm and your tummy. This is really important. The gap should be a finger-width.

4.   Close your eyes now.
5.   Focus on breathing in through the palm of your
        hand.
6.   Feel yourself drawing in breaths, through the
        palm of your hand.
7.   Remember how when you were inside your
        mummy, that's where your life support
        came into your body.
8.   You can breathe deep or shallow. Slow or fast.
        Whatever works.

Step 3

1.   Your eyes are still closed.
2.   Take the palm of your other hand.
3.   Place it over your chest.
4.   Make sure to leave a little gap between your
        palm and your chest. This is really important.
        The gap should be a finger-width.
5.   Focus on breathing out through the palm of
        your hand.
6.   Feel yourself pushing out breaths, through the
        palm of your hand.

You may feel some resistance to this breathing. That's
normal and fine. We call Steps 2 and 3 *Angel Wings*. Now,
we're going to focus the balance you're feeling on sleep
induction.

Step 4

1.   Open your eyes.
2.   Visualise yourself tossing and turning in bed, being unable to get properly to sleep.
3.   Now visualise something waking you up, then back to sleep, then waking you up again.
4.   You can run these visualisations like little movies in your head.
5.   Think whatever you are thinking, Feel whatever you are feeling.

Step 5

1.   Take the top two fingers of whatever is your writing hand.
2.   Place them on your forehead.
3.   Think whatever you are thinking, Feel whatever you are feeling.
4.   Try to think those visualisations. Really try.
5.   Keep trying for a few seconds. This can get really intense.

Step 6

1.   Take the palm of your writing hand.
2.   Place it over your tummy: just where your tum my button is.
3.   Make sure to leave a little gap between your palm and your tummy. This is really important. The gap should be a finger-width.
4.   Close your eyes now.

Step 7

1. Think whatever you are thinking, Feel whatever you are feeling.
2. Try to think those visualisations. Really try.

Step 8

1. Take your two fingers hand.
2. Open your palm and position over your chest: back to *Angel Wings*.
3. Breathe in *Angel Wings* for a few seconds.

Step 9

1. Now, you're going in a few moments to take a huge breath in.
2. Through your nose or your mouth.
3. However you'd do it if you were about to jump into a swimming pool.
4. Big breath in: *Now*.
5. Hold that breath for 3 long seconds.
6. One … Two … Three…
7. Let it out, and at the same time, press your palm into your chest.
8. You can fall back into a lying position, if you like.
9. Rest. Breathe normally.
10. Think whatever thoughts you think. Feel what ever feelings you feel.

Enjoy your sleep tonight.

End.

Explaining

Your getting to sleep problems come from you trying to repress your Anxiety during the day. You put a lot of effort into that repression.

You keep telling yourself that, if you don't do that, something terrible is going to happen. This makes it completely sensible to avoid wasting that investment by going to sleep, where you know you can't control that Anxiety.

So, you stay awake so you can keep your guard up against that awful Anxiety. Which makes you more tired. Which makes you feel even worse about your fear of that Anxiety running unchecked. This makes a vicious circle look like fun.

In this *Sleep Induction Technique,* first of all we balance you. That's what *Angel Wings* does.

Then, we get you to focus your thoughts, your energy, on disturbing your sleep. We get you to confront the thoughts of you - yes you - being responsible for those sleep-disturbing thoughts. We get you to own and own up to having those thoughts.

Next, we link those thoughts to Anxiety. The real thing, not the fake Stress that we use as an Anxiety repression tool.

Through Steps 8 and 9, your *Anxiety-Soothing Rhythm* ("ASR") blows away the fake Stress syndrome. Your ASR is the expert in balancing you, since the time you were born. The thoughts we conjure up to interfere with our ASR only work for a while. Our ASR is far stronger and smarter.

To use a medical metaphor, we have just activated the antibody for your fake Stress: the thing that interferes with your sleep engagement. Now, when you replay that fake Stress, your Anxiety "immune system" recognises it: and knocks it out.

You don't have to think or feel anything. It happens automatically.

After Care
As you get daily better engagement with sleep, the issue which brought you to use this *Sleep Induction Technique* simply disappears.

There no harm in repeating the Technique, if you like. Or if you sneakily manage to manufacture a new Stress fakery, which your Anxiety "immune system" needs to come to recognise, and disable.

5B   *Healing for Hyper*
Step 1
1.   Find some alone space.

2.   Sit down anywhere comfortable.

3.   You can do all this with your eyes open.

Step 2

1.   Take the palm of your writing hand.

2.   Place it hovering over your thigh.

3.   Make sure to leave a small gap of around a finger-width.

4.   Just notice whatever you notice.

5.   Move your hand away.

6.   Move it back.

Step 3

1.   Move your hand over your tummy: just where your tummy button is.

2.   Make sure to leave a small gap between your palm and your tummy. The gap should be a finger-width.

3.   Just notice whatever you notice.

4.   Maybe you can notice a difference between the sensation with your hand here; and when it was over your thigh.

Step 4

1.   Move your hand over your chest.

2.   Make sure to leave a small gap between your palm and your chest. The gap should be a finger-width.

3.   Just notice whatever you notice.

4.   Maybe you can notice a difference between the
         sensation with your hand here; and when it was
         over your tummy.

Step 5

1.   Move your hand back over your tummy.
2.   Hold it there for a few seconds.
3.   Then move your hand back to your thigh.
4.   Hold it there for a few seconds.
5.   Take your hand away and relax. Or go back to
         being hyper.

Step 6 (optional)

1.   When you're in bed, about to sleep, just place
         your palm – with gap – over your thigh (pause);
         tummy (pause); chest (pause); then back again.
2.   Just notice whatever you notice.
3.   Take your hand away and relax.

                              End.

Explaining

This Hyper state is – according to you, which is what
counts – stopping you from being able to sleep.

Now, it may be that there are very good reasons for you
not going to sleep tonight: you have an assignment to
complete, or you're at an all-night party. There's no rules
about this. You sleep when you want to. It's when you

want to, but can't, that it feels like a problem.

This Hyper state doesn't necessarily indicate that you're engaged in Anxiety repression. It can just be simply that you have a lot going on in your head, or that you're doing something active: or both.

What we're doing with this Technique is *convergence*. In each of the hand positions, you will be able to sense the energy of all of your body's cells, working together. The different hand positions allow you to focus on different power centres: your lower body; your tummy; your cardiac system.

Each of these has a distinct electrical signature that exists in the real world. EEG machines can actually pick up these signals and record them. So this is not spooky spiritual stuff we're doing here. It's science.

We are not dampening down your Hyper energy here. We are allowing your energy signatures of different parts of your body to *converge*: to meet each other. Step 6 suggests you do this just before you're ready to sleep, when you're lying on your bed.

You may get an extra burst of energy from this *convergence*. You might feel drawn into a relaxed, tranquil state. Either is fine. The point is that your mind has become aware that it's in sync with whatever is actually going on with the energy signals in your body.

After Care

This one is very much a "do it whenever you like" technique.

It's useful even apart from any sleep issues you may have. Sensing that *convergence* simply allows you to feel more You. That's what all Matrixial Healing is about.

6.   *Temporal Dream Therapy*

The interpretation of dreams is on a scientific par with the discernment of your future by poking around in animal entrails. It can be a brilliantly artistic and seductive Freudian enterprise: but then again so is Tarot reading.

But, in TDT, we don't pay much attention to the content of dreams.

We say that: *how we can dream determines what we dream.* Dreaming uses *the same brain* as waking. Just as it's the same body you take to bed. All that's different is that the "arrow of time" doesn't apply in dreamland: because your brain is not connected to time in the outside world.

It's like the *spatial* rules of a jigsaw puzzle being ignored at night time, so that the picture parts can go in table side down, instead of up: and still count as a valid part of the puzzle.

The only reason that you become troubled in dreams is that you're thinking thoughts that work under one arrow of time (say, backwards) but not the other way around. And vice versa.

All nightmares essentially resolve into two types:
- scenes involving Movement: running; being chased; running after; falling
- scenes about being stuck, and unable to move.

Come on, let's nail some nightmares.

6A   *Healing Scenario: Movement*

Step 1
1.   Close your eyes.
2.   Imagine you're having a recurrent dream about being chased.
3.   Just play your version of that dream, in your head.
4.   Stop.

Step 2
1.   See yourself getting into your car.
2.   It can be the car you have.
3.   Or a dream car: G Wagon, Rolls-Royce: whatever.
4.   Sit comfortably behind the wheel. Adjust your seat.
5.   It may be day or night: that's up to you.

Step 3

1. Look in your rear-view mirror.
2. Check that the road and space behind your car, is clear.
3. Open your eyes.
4. Blink a few times.

Step 4

1. Close your eyes.
2. Look in your rear-view mirror.
3. See yourself being chased.

Step 4

1. Focus through your rear-view mirror.
2. Try to play the nightmare movie of you being chased.

Step 5

1. Open your eyes.
2. Relax.

End.

Explaining

This is a very common dream. It can often be uncomfortable.

It's created by you trying to use your emotional headlights (which look into the future), to try and see the past. That's why you experience it as a nightmare.

The machinery for examining the past which you were born with, is your "rear-view mirror": that is, your subjective thinking.

You're asleep. So the usual time arrow signposts aren't there in your head. Which is why directions of time, and how your machinery follows them, gets mixed up. So, we simply point the correct machinery at the past.

Why is the "chased" scenario about the past? It isn't. It's a phantasm about a potential future experience. But it's being projected back into the past, so that you can engage your thoughts with it. That's why, when you point your backward-looking machinery at that projection: it disappears.

The nightmare scenario disappears. Clients report variations of:
- can see them in the rear-view mirror: but they are not running and are just frozen; or
- they are happily walking towards the rear of the car.

Neither of these is a nightmare scenario. It's just "shrug the shoulders" kind of odd, and doesn't matter. Since it doesn't matter, you forget about it.

You can simply adjust the Scenario to match what you remember from your nightmare: running; being chased;

chasing something; falling. In the latter case, park your car on the edge of a cliff or a multi-storey car park. In your head - don't actually do this!

After Care

Most clients report that the nightmare never comes back. If it does, then it's in the "shrug the shoulders" kind of odd way: so it doesn't feel emotionally troubling. Without that emotional attachment, it fades away, and stops coming back.

There's no harm in re-running the *Healing Scenario*. If you're dreams are no longer being broken by this nightmare scenario, you won't feel any need to fix it.

As a bonus, once you have rid yourself of this nightmare, the fear of it won't induce insomnia any more. You know that you can lie your head on the pillow and enjoy dreamland.

We still don't know what any of your actual nightmare sequence "means". But then again we don't actually know what anything we think "means". What we do know is that we can prevent ourselves from experiencing distressing mental images. Instantly.

6B   *Healing Scenario: Stuck*

Step 1

1.   Close your eyes.

2.   Imagine you're having a recurrent dream about being stuck.

3.   Could be stuck in a room; or kidnapped; or stuck in a loop of repeated activity.

4.   Just play your version of that dream, in your head.

5.   Stop.

Step 2

1.   See yourself getting into your car.

2.   It can be the car you have.

3.   Or a dream car: G Wagon, Rolls-Royce: whatever.

4.   Sit comfortably behind the wheel. Adjust your seat.

5.   It's dusk or night time.

Step 3

1.   Turn your headlights on.

2.   Check that the road and space in front of your car is clear.

3.   Open your eyes.

4.   Blink a few times.

Step 4

1.   Close your eyes

2.   Look through your windscreen at whatever you can see in your headlights.

3.   See yourself being stuck.

Step 5

1.   Focus through your headlights.
2.   Try to play the nightmare movie of you being stuck.

Step 6

1.   Open your eyes.
2.   Relax.

End.

Explaining

This is another common uncomfortable dream.

It's created by you trying to use your rear-view mirror (which looks into the past), to try and see the future. That's why you experience it as a nightmare.

The machinery for looking into the future, which you were born with, is your "headlights": that is, your emotional system.

You're asleep. So the usual time-arrow signposts aren't there in your head. Which is why directions of time, and how your machinery follows them, gets mixed up. So, we simply point the correct machinery at the future.

Why is the "stuck" scenario about the future? It isn't. It's a phantasm about a past experience. But it's being projected into the future, so that you can emotionally engage with it. That's why, when you point your forward-looking machinery at that projection: it disappears.

The nightmare scenario disappears. Clients report variations of:

- a dim outline of the stuck scenario; or
- can't see the scenario at all; or
- they just see themselves standing up, or floating: generally being free.

Neither of these is a nightmare scenario. It's just "shrug the shoulders" kind of odd, and doesn't matter. Since it doesn't matter, you forget about it.

You can simply adjust the Scenario to match what you remember from your nightmare.

After Care

Most clients report that the nightmare never comes back. If it does, then it's in the "shrug the shoulders" kind of odd way: so it doesn't feel emotionally troubling. Without that thinking activity wrapped around it, it fades away and doesn't come back.

Again, there's no harm in re-running the *Healing Scenario*. And, once you have rid yourself of this nightmare, the fear of it won't induce insomnia any more. You know that you can lie your head on the pillow and enjoy dreamland.

We still don't know what any of your actual nightmare sequence "means". But then again we don't actually know what anything we think "means". What we do know is that we can prevent ourselves from experiencing distressing mental images. Instantly.

7.   *Waking Fatigue Release*

We all feel a bit weird sometimes, when we wake up. We're coming out of a place where we have not been experiencing our mental link with time. So, feelings of disorientation are normal.

You₂

Here, we are going to be using the *You₂* idea. When you're asked to connect with You₂, what this means is: thinking of a second You. That's just You: not older or younger you, or a relative. It's just You, as You are, right now.

It seems strange to read this. Just try it, right now.

> *Close your eyes.*
> *Think of second You: You₂.*
> *Just allow your head to connect with the head of You₂.*

If you did that: you've done it. There's that *You₂* connection. You can sense it.

Scenario

Clients can report that they feel worse than this, though. Experiencing feelings of:

- tiredness
- little aches and pains

Let's cure the waking blues.

Healing

Step 1

1.   You can stay in bed, or sit on the side, or stand and have a stretch. Whatever works for you.
2.   Keep your eyes open.

Step 2

1.   Take the top two fingers of whatever is your writing hand.
2.   Place those fingers gently on the back of your neck, on the same side. Anywhere between your hairline and collar bone.
3.   Rest your fingers at that spot.
4.   Breathe normally.

Step 3

1.   Feel a connection, in your head, with Second You: You$_2$.
2.   This is just you: yourself, looking at you.
3.   Like You$_2$ is somewhere around the edge of your elbow.
4.   Allow You$_2$'s head to connect with yours.

Step 4

1.   Now, allow You₂ to look into you: from your
        head, down to your toes.
2.   Feel You₂'s breathing.
3.   Match the rhythm of your breathing with You₂'s
        breathing.
4.   While you're matching that breathing, look with
        You₂ into you: from your head, down to your
        toes.

Step 5

1.   Let the You₂ connection drop.
2.   Relax.

                              End.

Explaining

You're feeling the tiredness, aches and pains, because you're not fully synchronised with external time. That sounds a bit odd, written like that. But it's just saying, in plain English, the technical version you can read more about in Part 2 *Healing How*.

The *You₂ Avatar* is that part of your brain (which we call Theta Θ), which is always objectively connected with external reality. Your subjective thoughts of things (including thoughts about tiredness and pain) happen in another part of your brain (which we call /S/).

In this *Technique*, we are getting you to engage the

subjective part of your brain with the objective part. That enables you to get "in sync". The tiredness, aches and pains are real for you, but only through a part of your brain. The other part doesn't recognise them.

You get those two parts of your brain to engage with each other. The tiredness, aches and pains, just disappear: instantly.

After Care
You can use this morning refresher whenever you like.

The tiredness, aches and pains don't come from anything you're doing "wrong" with yourself. They are a natural effect of moving from timeless sleep, to time-directional waking. So you're likely to experience the same symptoms on lots of days. But that's OK now: you can You$_2$ the morning blues away.

CHAPTER 3

MEMORY TRAUMA

Matrixial Memory analysis is that we don't store memories in a filing cabinet. We don't lug around suitcases full of baggage from childhood "wounds". There's a detailed explanation in *Secret Self*, Chapter 11.

We have patterns in our objective (Theta Θ) "cloud": our "computer brain". Like stars in the sky.

PISCES

https://www.amazon.co.uk/Pisces-Constellation-Astrology-Horoscope-Journal/dp/1729585345

Our subjective mind can look up at those stars and see whatever we want to in them. We get into habits of seeing the patterns one way. But it's just what we choose to see: every day.

There's a connection to external time outside of ourselves as well. That's why we replay our memories differently when we're asleep. Our subjective thinking - the brain place we create memories of things - is always looking backwards. It's our rear-view mirror. looking into the past.

The reality is that all of our subjective thinking is an act of memory. We manufacture present meanings using the same brain process by which we construct past meanings. We call one (if we call it anything) "contemporary cognition", and we call the other Memory.

But they are the same process, within the same Systems Architecture. We simply choose what we decide to think of, when we look at those stars: when we engage with the Theta Θ "cloud".

At the ordinary experience level, we are well-used to the idea that environment influences not only our present thoughts, but our Memory.

The "internal environment" of the Self, as we pass through our life years of experience, effects change in our Memory patterns: our {ident} associations. What you once remembered with love, you now remember with antipathy: and vice versa.

71

Our identification of Memory states, one with another, is an act of equivalence.

- We look at the "night sky" there in our objective mind.
- We create thoughts about it in our subjective mind.
- Also, in our subjective mind, we can assign meanings to the thoughts: by attaching "feelings" to those thoughts.

With this understanding of how Memory works, we can change how we re-create Memory. This can change our lives.

8.   *Wiping Traumatic Memory*

Scenario

Many clients report traumatic memories:

- I don't like to get peaceful, because I get bad memories coming back
- I feel very burdened by past memories.
- I get anxious about bad memories coming back

We are not concerned with the details of those memories. You already know what your troubling memories are. We don't need to know.

That sort of therapy that involves you picking over old scars, operates at a level somewhere between useless and harmful.

Healing

Step 1

1.   You can sit down, or stand. Whatever works for you.
2.   Close your eyes.
3.   Go inside your head.
4.   Choose One memory: one that troubles you. Whatever it is.

Step 2

1.   See a video or cinema screen.
2.   Play that One memory on that screen.
3.   See what you see. Hear what you hear. Feel what you feel.
4.   This just takes a few seconds. You can replay a 10-hour scene, in 10 seconds.
5.   Rewind the film to the start.
6.   Press Play again.
7.   Now: hit the pause button.
8.   Just leave the video there. You know you can come back to it anytime.

Step 3

1.   Feel a connection, in your head, with Second You: You$_2$.
2.   This is just you: yourself, looking at you.
3.   You2 is a few arm-lengths away. Like they're standing at the other side of whatever room you're in.

4.   Allow You$_2$'s head to connect with yours.

Step 4

1.   You$_2$ can see your head.
2.   You$_2$ can see you looking at the screen.
3.   You$_2$ can see the space between you and the
        screen: the distance between you and the screen.

Step 5

1.   Feel a connection: between You$_2$ and you.
2.   Feel You$_2$ watching you.
3.   Feel You$_2$ watching you, as you look at the
        screen.
4.   Feel You$_2$ feeling the space between you and the
        screen: the distance between you and the screen.

Step 6

1.   You$_2$ can see your head.
2.   You$_2$ can see you looking at the screen.
3.   You$_2$ can see the space between you and the
        screen: the distance between you and the screen.

Step 7

1.   Now: reach out, and press Play.
2.   OK: relax.
3.   Now: try again to press Play.
4.   The screen images are blurry, or you just can't
        press Play at all. That's OK.
5.   Now: try again to press Play.

Step 8

1.   OK: relax
2.   Open your eyes.
3.   Breathe.

Step 9

1.   Breathe again: just normally.
2.   Close your eyes.
3.   Think of a happy memory: from when you were
        5-7. Anything happy, big or small.
4.   Now, think of a happy memory: from when you
        were 11-13. Anything happy, big or small.
5.   And, think of a happy memory: from when you
        were 15-17. Anything happy, big or small.
6.   Just let the happy memories swirl around, like
        different flavours of ice cream, in a tub.

Step 10

1.   Now: back to the video.
2.   Try again to press Play
3.   All you're getting back is "ice cream" swirl
        memories. That's fine.
4.   Open your eyes.
5.   Relax.

End.

Explaining
Right now, a little "sub-routine" in your head, is scurrying

around, looking for those lost memories. It's like that feeling when you know your keys are in the house somewhere, but you just can't find them.

But there's a big difference: those keys are there somewhere. But the memories have gone.

Empirical tests have shown that the memory loss is permanent. Over periods of weeks and months: the memories don't come back. That the *Psychotectic* longitudinal effect.

You can remember Facts: just like facts about history; or biographical facts like your birth date or address. But they don't *mean* anything. They are just facts. You don't attach "emotions" to them. You can if you like, but it seems pretty pointless to try.

Now:
• go look for the cover pic for that bad Memory video: OK, that's gone too.

And:
• check out the library where you used to keep the video: no, that's gone as well.

You kind of know where it used to be. But now it's like a closed door at the end of a corridor: and the corridor is fading away.

You'll keep running that "try and find it" sub-routine for a few days. That's natural. You've created a habit of marking that "library" on your mental map, so you can always have quick access to it. But now the contents it used to house, have gone. So the library has gone too.

After Care
Now:

How Do You Feel?

The usual response is a combination of:
- kind of empty but not really
- like a weight's been lifted
- feeling the need to smile
- feeling a sudden burst of energy

All this good stuff: it stays with you. For days and weeks and months.

We never mention to the Client that the specific traumatic memory which you chose to work with: *it's connected to all your other traumatic memories*.

Now:

- Go have a look for another traumatic memory: it's gone.
- Go look for the cover pic for that bad Memory video: OK, that's gone too.

And:

- Check out the library where you used to keep the video: no, that's gone as well.

You kind of know where it used to be. But now it's like a closed door at the end of a corridor: and the corridor is fading away.

Every time you go looking for one of those bad memories, all you get back is "not there" and a temptation to feel "ice cream" sensations.

It's not strictly necessary to give you that "ice cream" memories connection. But it feeds the sniffer dog that your sub-routine sends out in hunt of memories. If you like to think of it this way (which is technically really incorrect), the "ice cream" memories "fill the gap" left in your memory bank.

Yet, you will do what we all do. Manufacture more "memories" as make-believe reality. That's fine. Because now, if you make up traumatic memories, you can just go lose them: as you did with whatever memory you used in the Steps.

9.   PTSD Relief

Let's get some definition of PTSD and its effects, from the
Royal College of Psychiatrists (RCP):[4]

What is PTSD?

In our everyday lives, any of us can have an experience that is
overwhelming, frightening, and beyond our control. We could find
ourselves in a car crash, be the victim of an assault, or see an
accident. Police, fire brigade or ambulance workers are more likely to
have such experiences – they often have to deal with horrifying scenes.
Soldiers may be shot or blown up, and see friends killed or injured. Most
people, in time, get over experiences like this without needing help.
In some people, though, traumatic experiences set off a reaction that
can last for many months or years. This is called Post-traumatic Stress
Disorder, or PTSD for short.

What is complex PTSD?

People who have repeatedly experienced:

•   severe neglect or abuse as an adult or as a child
•   severe repeated violence or abuse as an adult, such as torture or
abusive imprisonment

can have a similar set of reactions. This is called 'complex PTSD' and is
described in more detail below.

How does PTSD start?

PTSD can start after any traumatic event. A traumatic event is one
where you see that you are in danger, your life is threatened, or
where you see other people dying or being injured. Typical traumatic
events would be:

•   serious accidents
•   military combat
•   violent personal assault (sexual assault, physical attack,
        abuse, robbery, mugging)
•   being taken hostage
•   terrorist attack
•   being a prisoner-of-war

---

[4] https://www.rcpsych.ac.uk/mental-health/problems-disorders/post-traumatic-stress-disorder

- natural or man-made disasters
- being diagnosed with a life-threatening illness.

Even hearing about the unexpected injury or violent death of a family member or close friend can start PTSD.

When does PTSD start? The symptoms of PTSD can start immediately or after a delay of weeks or months, but usually within 6 months of the traumatic event.

What does PTSD feel like?
Many people feel grief-stricken, depressed, anxious, guilty and angry after a traumatic experience. As well as these understandable emotional reactions, there are three main types of symptoms:

Flashbacks & nightmares
You find yourself re-living the event, again and again. This can happen both as a 'flashback' in the day and as nightmares when you are asleep.

These can be so realistic that it feels as though you are living through the experience all over again. You see it in your mind, but may also feel the emotions and physical sensations of what happened - fear, sweating, smells, sounds, pain.

Ordinary things can trigger off flashbacks. For instance, if you had a car crash in the rain, a rainy day might start a flashback.

Avoidance & numbing
It can be just too upsetting to re-live your experience over and over again. So you distract yourself. You keep your mind busy by losing yourself in a hobby, working very hard, or spending your time absorbed in crosswords or jigsaw puzzles. You avoid places and people that remind you of the trauma, and try not to talk about it.

You may deal with the pain of your feelings by trying to feel nothing at all – by becoming emotionally numb. You communicate less with other people who then find it hard to live or work with you.

Being 'on guard'

You find that you stay alert all the time, as if you are looking out for danger. You can't relax. This is called 'hypervigilance'. You feel anxious and find it hard to sleep. Other people will notice that you are jumpy and irritable.

Other symptoms
- muscle aches and pains
- diarrhoea
- irregular heartbeats
- headaches
- feelings of panic and fear
- *depression*
- drinking too much alcohol
- using drugs (including painkillers).

It's worth reading the rest of this excellent RCP summary. The standard approach to treatment is also explained:

All the effective psychotherapies for PTSD focus on the traumatic experience – or experiences - rather than your past life. You cannot change or forget what has happened. You can learn to think differently about it, about the world, and about your life.

You need to be able to remember what happened, as fully as possible, without being overwhelmed by fear and distress.

These therapies help you to put your experiences into words. By remembering the event, going over it and making sense of it, your mind can do its normal job of storing the memories away, and moving on to other things.

When you start to feel safer, and more in control of your feelings, you won't need to avoid the memories as much. You will be able to only think about them when you want to, rather than having them burst into your mind out of the blue.

All these treatments should all be given by PTSD specialists. The sessions should be at least weekly, with the same therapist, for 8-12 weeks. Although sessions will usually last around an hour, they can sometimes last up to 90 minutes.

> *Cognitive Behavioural Therapy* (CBT) is a talking treatment which can help us to understand how 'habits of thinking' can make the PTSD worse - or even cause it. CBT can help you change these 'extreme' ways of thinking, which can also help you to feel better and to behave differently.

In Matrixial Therapy, we do agree that PTSD involves issues around Memory. As you'll know from the Healing for *Wiping Traumatic Memory*, we don't believe it's a good idea to try and "face" a bad memory.

After all, it's not like visiting a museum: an actual collection of past things. Every act of remembering is an act of creation: looking up at those stars. Or, in the case of PTSD, looking down into the flames of your hellish personal experience.

When we "access a memory", we are creating a set of thoughts and feelings in our subjective mind, by reference to a set of patterns in our objective brain: the cloud. We can volunteer to do this, and we can be "triggered" into doing it, by our daily experiences in the world.

In PTSD, we experience problems with this process. *Matrixial Healing* doesn't try to get you to "confront" traumatic memories. Why would we need or want to? You're doing that to yourself repeatedly: that's why you're seeking help. The confrontation approach can seem like taking an alcoholic to a cocktail bar, for their first recovery session: there's your problem – now confront it.

Instead, we focus on getting the memory creation process to go right again: and that's what heals the trauma. What's going wrong with the memory creation process is the same for everyone who's suffering PTSD: that's why mind science can categorise a person as suffering from that condition, in the first place.

Scenario

A typical Client self-reports flashback memories of one or more traumatic episodes. The Client may self-report various trigger situations. We will deal with those separately.

PTSD is a condition which is made up of layers of linked problems. So we use a series of Step Parts, to build the total remedy.

The intensity of the Client's experiences, and the power of the Healing release, make it important that a Practitioner is there to help the process.

Healing

PART 1

Step 1

1.   You can sit down, or stand. Whatever works for you.

2.   Close your eyes.

3.   Go inside your head.

4.   Choose One memory: one that troubles you.

Whatever it is.

5.　**Please <u>don't</u> focus on whatever is the central traumatic Memory which you have problems with.**

6.　Please focus on some other troubling Memory.

Step 2

1.　See a video or cinema screen.

2.　Play that One memory on that screen.

3.　See what you see. Hear what you hear. Feel what you feel.

4.　This just takes a few seconds. You can replay a 10 hour scene, in 10 seconds.

5.　Rewind the film to the start.

6.　Press Play again.

7.　Now: hit the pause button.

8.　Just leave the video there. You know you can come back to it anytime.

Step 3

1.　Feel a connection, in your head, with Second You: You_2.

2.　This is just you: yourself, looking at you.

3.　You_2 is a few arm-lengths away. Like they're standing at the other side of whatever room you're in.

4.　Allow You_2's head to connect with yours.

Step 4

1. You$_2$ can see your head. You$_2$ can see you looking at the screen.
2. You$_2$ can see the space between you and the screen: the distance between you and the screen.

Step 5

1. Feel a connection: between You$_2$ and you.
2. Feel You$_2$ watching you.
3. Feel You$_2$ watching you, as you look at the screen.
4. Feel You$_2$ feeling the space between you and the screen: the distance between you and the screen.

Step 6

1. You$_2$ can see your head.
2. You$_2$ can see you looking at the screen.
3. You$_2$ can see the space between you and the screen: the distance between you and the screen.

Step 7

1. Now: reach out, and press Play on the video.
2. OK: relax.
3. Now: try again to press Play.
4. The screen images are blurry, or you just can't press Play at all. That's OK.
5. Now: try again to press Play.

Step 8

1.   OK: relax
2.   Open your eyes.
3.   Breathe.

End.

PART 2

Step 1

1.   You can stay in bed, or sit on the side, or stand
      and have a stretch. Whatever works for you.
2.   Keep your eyes open.

Step 2

1.   Feel a connection, in your head, with Second
      You: You$_2$.
2.   This is just you: yourself, looking at you.
3.   You$_2$ is just over your shoulder.
4.   Allow You$_2$'s head to connect with yours.

Step 3

1.   Take the top two fingers of whatever is your
      writing hand.
2.   **Now: whatever is the central traumatic**
      Memory which you have problems with:
         just touch your 2 fingers to the place on your
         body where you first feel that Memory.
         Maybe:
            your head; or your chest;
            your stomach; your back; or

below the waist (in which
case just touch the top of
either thigh).

3.   Gently hold your 2 fingers at that point.

Step 4

1.   Breathe again: just normally.
2.   Close your eyes.
3.   Look inside You$_2$'s head. There are all the
Memories there, that you also have.
4.   Please find a happy memory in You$_2$: from when
You$_2$ was 5-7. Anything happy, big or small.
Please go look now.
5.   Feel the connection between the place that your
2 fingers are touching, and inside the
head of You$_2$.
6.   Now, slowly allow the feelings of that place
your fingers are touching, to move up
that connection to You$_2$.
7.   Allow the feelings of that place your fingers are
touching, to connect with that happy memory
inside You$_2$'s head.
8.   Allow that connection between that happy
memory inside You$_2$'s head and your
fingers touching place.
9.   Now, you can allow that connection to get
stronger. And stronger.
10.   Think whatever you feel like thinking. Feel
whatever you think you're feeling.

87

11. Relax.
12. Move your fingers away and flex them.
13. Open your eyes.
14. Breathe.

Step 5

1. Please find a happy memory in You$_2$: from when You$_2$ was 11-13. Anything happy, big or small.
2. Take 2 fingers of the hand you write with.
3. Touch your 2 fingers to the place on your body where you first feel **any** bad Memory.
4. Breathe again: just normally.
5. Close your eyes.
6. Look inside You$_2$'s head. There are all the Memories there, that you also have.
7. Please find a happy memory in You$_2$: from when You$_2$ was 11-13. Anything happy, big or small. Please go look now.
8. Feel the connection between the place that your 2 fingers are touching, and inside the head of You$_2$.
9. Now, slowly allow the feelings of that place your fingers are touching, to move up that connection to You$_2$.
10. Allow the feelings of that place your fingers are touching, to connect with that happy memory inside You$_2$'s head.
11. Allow that connection between that happy memory inside You$_2$'s head and your

fingers touching place.

12.   Now, you can allow that connection to get stronger. And stronger.

13.   Think whatever you feel like thinking. Feel whatever you think you're feeling.

14.   Relax.

15.   Move your fingers away and flex them.

16.   Open your eyes.

17.   Breathe.

Step 6

1.   Please find a happy memory in You$_2$: from when You$_2$ was 11-13. Anything happy, big or small.

2.   Take the top two fingers of whatever is your writing hand.

3.   Touch your 2 fingers to the place on your body where you first feel **any** bad Memory.

4.   Take 2 fingers of your non-writing hand.

5.   Touch your 2 fingers to the place on your body where you first feel **any** bad Memory: the **same** Memory.

6.   Breathe again: just normally.

7.   Close your eyes.

8.   Look inside You$_2$'s head. There are all the Memories there, that you also have.

9.   Please find a happy memory in You$_2$: from when You$_2$ was 15-17. Anything happy, big or small. Please go look now.

10.   Feel the connection between the place that your

Right hand 2 fingers are touching, and
 inside the head of You$_2$.
and
Feel the connection between the place that your
Left hand hand 2 fingers are touching,
and inside the head of You$_2$.

11. Now, slowly allow the feelings of the places
your 4 fingers are touching, to move up
that connection to You$_2$.

12. Allow the feelings of the places your 4 fingers
are touching, to connect with that happy
memory inside You$_2$'s head.

13. Allow that connection between that happy
memory inside You$_2$'s head and your 4
fingers touching places.

14. Now, you can allow that connection to get
stronger. And stronger.

15. Think whatever you feel like thinking. Feel
whatever you think you're feeling.

16. Relax.

17. Move your fingers away and flex them.

18. Open your eyes.

19. Breathe.

End.

PART 3

Step 1

1.   Find some alone space.
2.   Sit down anywhere comfortable.
3.   Take the top two fingers of whatever is your
        writing hand.
4.   Place those fingers gently on the waist side
        of your tummy. (You can find the location
        simply by placing your two fingers over your
        belly button, then moving them around to your
        writing hand side).
5.   Rest your fingers at that spot.
6.   Close your eyes.
7.   Breathe normally.

Step 2

1.   Take the top two fingers of your other hand.
2.   Place them gently at the back of your neck, on
        the other side of your body from your other
        fingers. (Location is anywhere between the nape
        of your neck and your collar-bone: just
        gently move your fingers till you find a spot that
        feels fine to you).
3.   Breathe normally.

Step 3: Take 1 to 2 Minutes

1.   Feel a connection between your fingers.
2.   A connection running through your upper body.
        Like a wire.

3.   You may feel it hot. You may feel it cold.
4.   If it's a hot connection, allow it to get hotter. If it's a cold connection, allow it to get colder.
5.   Allow the connection to become more intense.
6.   Feel it like the filament in a light bulb, getting brighter as you turn up the voltage.
7.   Allow yourself to allow those toxic energy feelings to run through that connection.
8.   Between your fingers, it feels like angry electric ants scurrying around.
9.   It feels like the connection is becoming barbed wire, spilling toxic chemicals into your body.
10.   Let the angry energy become more intense.
11.   And more. Filling your chest and your head.

Step 4
1.   Now it's coursing through you. That toxic writhing energy.
2.   Take the hand with the fingers which are at your waist.
3.   Take the palm of that hand.
4.   Place it gently over the centre of your chest.
5.   Still feel the angry toxic energy coursing through you.

Step 5
1.   Now, you're going in a few moments to take a huge breath in.
2.   Through your nose or your mouth.

3.   However you'd do it if you were about to jump into a swimming pool.
4.   Big breath in: *Now.*
5.   Hold that breath for 3 long seconds.
6.   One … Two … Three…
7.   Let it out, and at the same time, press your palm into your chest.
8.   You can fall back into your chair, or into a lying position, if you like.
9.   Rest. Breathe normally.
10.   Think whatever thoughts you think. Feel what ever feelings you feel.

End.

PART 4

Step 1
1.   Find some alone space.
2.   Sit down anywhere comfortable.

Step 2
1.   Please focus on the thoughts and feelings you have, when your guard is up.
2.   The thoughts and feelings you use to keep control.
3.   The thoughts which protect you from unpleasant feelings.
4.   Allow those thoughts and feelings to swirl around, for a few moments.

Step 3

1.   In the next Steps, you can keep your eyes open.

2.   Or you can close them if it feels OK to do that.

Step 4

1.   Take the palm of your writing hand.

2.   Place it over your tummy: just where your tummy button is.

3.   Make sure to leave a little gap between your palm and your tummy. This is really important. The gap should be a finger-width.

4.   Focus on breathing in through the palm of your hand.

5.   Feel yourself drawing in breaths, through the palm of your hand.

6.   Remember how when you were inside your mummy, that's where your life support came into your body.

7.   You can breathe deep or shallow. Slow or fast. Whatever works.

8.   Your eyes can still be open. Or closed. Whatever is OK for you.

Step 5

1.   Take the palm of your other hand.

2.   Place it over your chest.

3.   Make sure to leave a little gap between your palm and your chest. This is really important. The gap should be a finger-width.

4.   Focus on breathing out through the palm of
        your hand.
5.   Feel yourself pushing out breaths, through the
        palm of your hand.
6.   Relax your hands.
7.   If you had closed your eyes, feel free to open
        them.

You may feel some resistance to this breathing. That's
normal and fine.
We call Steps 4 and 5 *Angel Wings*.

Step 6

1.   Now, please review the history of your head.
2.   Just de-focus, with your eyes open.
3.   During Steps 4 and 5, did you feel like your
        head was just emptying?
4.   Your thoughts like dancers on a crowded dance
        floor: all moving to the sides of the room
        and leaving an empty space, when band stopped
        playing.
5.   Now, please go back to that time in your head.
        The empty space, filled with feelings of peace,
        balance and power.
6.   If it's easier to close your eyes, that's OK.
7.   Please look for the place that the crowded
        thoughts and feelings went to.
8.   Just have a look. Maybe it's nowhere. Maybe
        they just disappeared. You can choose.

9.   Now, just relax.

10.   Breathe.

11.   Get up and have a stretch.

End.

Explaining

Part 1 you're already familiar with: the standard *Memory Wipe*. But, since we are trying to help people to feel better, not worse, we don't have them play a movie of whatever Memory is central to their PTSD.

We don't need to. *All bad Memory experiences are connected: they use the same process.* You know how expensive clothes on a shop rack have those little chains connecting them. It's kind of like that.

So, when we adjust the Memory process for one bad Memory, the others "on the chain" get adjusted automatically. By using the Steps in Part 1, we have automatically adjusted the central PTSD origin Memory. Without going anywhere near it in our heads.

Part 2 is about the physical connection between the central PTSD origin Memory, and the body. We are bypassing the subjective mind (where all the trouble is), and connecting body impulses to the objective "cloud" part of the mind.

We are getting the Client to re-connect their senses (the finger-touching places) to the process which associates those senses with happy memories. After all, we only have the senses we have. They do the same work, whether we are being washed by pouring rain, or basking in glowing sunshine.

We have simply got into a habit of associating sensory inputs with ideas in our head. So we change how those associations are constructed, by going through the 3 age-range processes.

Part 3 is the familiar Anxiety remedy. There is no way we would attempt this, before we had done Parts 1 and 2. It would be too traumatic, and the mind-body would just shut down and refuse to allow the Anxiety to action.

Now we have disconnected whatever Memory is central to their PTSD, from the body sensations which were being used to keep it going, we can safely use the Anxiety pump.

Now, we need to balance. We also need to expose to the mind the non-reality of the thoughts and feelings which seem so real, under the repeated crushing weight of the traumatic Memory-Sensation linkage.

So, in Part 4, we invite those thoughts and feelings to try and stay "on the dancefloor", when the body's Biomorphic energy forces are turning off the dance music.

Part of the PTSD problem is a disabling lack of confidence

in the ability of our mind and body to cope. To cope with the damage that we are self-inflicting. So, we try to keep control of our thoughts and feelings, channelling them into narrow bands to try and achieve that.

This is why we invite the Client to go back into "empty dancefloor" head, and try to find where those thoughts and feelings went to. It's a bit like the invitation, in the standard *Memory Wipe*, to go look for the now lost Memory and its cover image.

In Part 4, the Client comes to realise that they actually can't find those narrow band control thoughts and feelings. Well, they sort of can. But instead of being sharp and defined and very useful as "walls", they are vague and fuzzy, and useless as anything.

At the same time, the Client experiences those classic Matrixial feelings of balance, peace and power. The sense that control comes out of those feelings, rather than control being something you do, in order to get something like peace, in a narrow band of mind.

This is a lot to pack in. It is better to do this all in one session, if we can. It still only takes around an hour, all in. It's less exhausting than the multi-numbered Steps make it look. That's because, all the way through, those feelings of balance, peace and power grow during the session, making each step easier.

After Care

The Client will usually feel a combination of exhilaration, and exhaustion.

It does come as something of a shock to realise that a coping strategy we have been using for a long time, was the problem, rather than a solution.

Now, it's time for the client to enjoy some life experiences: whether in baby-steps or bigger ones.

In the meantime, the Client can expect to experience a few days of disorientation. After all, they have just thrown away a badly working compass, and are now life-route finding by themselves: and much better for it.

The Client will find it really helpful to practice *Angel Wings*. Can be as much as every hour, if that works for them. Or as little as every few days. Who wouldn't want to feel balance, peace and power: whenever you want.

There can be cases where the PTSD has become overlayered with other issues, as the RCP web entry says:

- muscle aches and pains
- diarrhoea
- irregular heartbeats
- headaches
- feelings of panic and fear
- depression
- drinking too much alcohol
- using drugs (including painkillers).

We can deal with these, under the Healing topics looked at elsewhere in this book.

The first group above all fall under *Symptomatic Relief* Chapter.
Panic and fear antidotes fall under *Anxiety Issues Healing*.
The third collection are dealt with in the *Addiction Issues* Chapter.

It would be very unusual to find that we need to repeat the collection of *Healings* in this section. Once we have adjusted the process of Memory creation, that adjustment is permanent.

It doesn't mean that we won't ever again begin to experience problems with that process. The machinery has got dinted: and that's why we experience problems in the first place.

But that machinery started out perfect: when we were born. It's incredibly tough and resilient. It's made to grow and adapt. It's way stronger than anything we can think of. Our *Healing* is just a way of letting that perfect system do its work for you: so you don't have to keep trying.

10. *Restoring Memory*

We're not dealing here with a condition of serious amnesia. Nor people who want to recover what they believe are traumatic memories.

Instead, we're helping to "fill out" sketchy memories of nice events. We know that we can provide effective *Healing* for traumatic memories. Why not help people to experience the best of their past life?

Scenario

A Client self-reports that they have no problem remembering bad stuff that's happened. But they have trouble remembering nice past experiences.

Healing

Step 1

1.   Close your eyes.
2.   Think of the outline of the Memory that you're looking for.
3.   Just the outline edges of it, in your head.
4.   Stop.

Step 2

1.   See yourself getting into your own car.
2.   It can be the car you have.
3.   Or a dream car: G Wagon, Rolls-Royce: whatever.
4.   Sit comfortably behind the wheel. Adjust your seat.
5.   It may be day or night: that's up to you.

Step 3

1.   Look in your rear-view mirror.

2.   Check that the road and space behind your car,
      is clear.
3.   Open your eyes.
4.   Blink a few times.

Step 4

1.   Feel a connection, in your head, with Second
      You: You$_2$.
2.   This is just you: yourself, looking at you.
3.   You$_2$ is in the passenger seat, next to you.
4.   Allow You$_2$'s head to connect with yours.

Step 5

1.   You$_2$ can see your head.
2.   You$_2$ can see you looking in the rear-view mirror.
3.   You$_2$ can see the space between the rear-view
      mirror and outside the car: the distance between
      you and the places back down the road.

Step 6

1.   Feel a connection: between You$_2$ and you.
2.   Feel You$_2$ watching you.
3.   Feel You$_2$ watching you, as you look in the rear-
      view mirror.
4.   Feel You$_2$ feeling the space between your rear-
      view mirror and the places back down the road.

Step 7

1.   Now, allow You$_2$ to see the memories you're

looking for, appearing on the rear-view mirror.

2.   Let the rear-view mirror expand, as it fills with those memories.

3.   Allow the rear-view mirror to become as big an iPad screen.

4.   Then as big a TV screen.

5.   Then as big as a cinema screen at a drive-in movie.

Step 8

1.   You need to switch your headlights on, to see that drive-in movie screen.

2.   Switch your headlights on.

3.   See the details of those memories: the sights, the sounds, the feelings. The colours, the smells.

4.   Just sit back, with You$_2$ beside you, and allow both of your heads to connect.

5.   Enjoy the show.

Step 9

1.   Open your eyes.

2.   Relax.

End.

Explaining

You can see that we are using a version of *Temporal Dream Therapy*. But now, we are using the TDT connections in a very different way.

Now, we are re-connecting thoughts and feelings to the "star sky": the objective "cloud" in the brain.

We understand that, inside the subjective mind, the Client can't find the connections that they want (between what we call {idents}). You could spend your life looking for connections in your subjective mind: as we all do.

But each time you do make an equalisation (matching one {ident} with another), you create a new relationship of ideas. That then creates another layer which can obscure what it is you're trying to look for.

So, in Steps 1-3, we clear the subjective mind, and create what we call <coherence>. Then we use the You2 Avatar to switch on the connection with the objective mind.

There was an original experience, which was capable of creating a "star pattern" connection to the subjective mind. By using the You2 Avatar, and getting it, rather than your subjective mind to "look for memory", you get to re-create the connections formed in that original experience.

We then allow you, in Steps 7 and 8, to reconnect with the potential richness of the original experience memory.

After Care
Once you have re-established these connections, they are as permanent as you want them to be. Obviously, the more you revisit those memory connections, the easier it will become for you to do that.

And, of course, you can use this technique for other happy memories that you'd like to rediscover.

CHAPTER 4

RELATIONSHIP TRAUMA

We could do a whole book on this. In a way, we have. Enjoying and coping with relationships works better when you can experience these things for yourself: balance, peace and power.

You're not going to get any of these from anybody else. A relationship unbalances: whether in the honeymoon or the divorce stage. It's a Challenge to your Slices, particularly: Needs/Wants, Chemistry, Empathy and Security. When it stops being a challenge, it stops being a relationship. That Challenge is a good thing. It's how we learn and grow.

A relationship doesn't give peace. Peace is what you can bring out of a relationship, but it's always conditional upon that Challenge and the responses of all parties.

Relationships involve power negotiations. These understandings, conflicts and agreements can disempower you, as against another, or empower you.

In Matrixial Therapy, we focus on You. The more grounded you are in your own capacity to experience balance, peace and power, the more you can give and get from any relationship.

We don't subscribe to theories of relationship dynamics. Not beyond the essential analysis that: we are all born into, and nurtured by dependence. We grow to adulthood under relationships of dependency. Since that's true for everyone – even Tarzan among the apes – it's difficult to see how this universal truth offers us any answers to anything.

Every one of us experiences that dependency differently. Even siblings in the same family. So, it's also difficult to see how each individual experience can be turned into a general theory.

What we do say is that, the more aware you are of how your Personality Slices are working – or not working – together, the more psychologically capable you'll be. The more balance, peace and power, you can experience.

People recognise those qualities in others. It's attractive. It's what looks – from the outside – like self-confidence.

11.   *Obsession*

We explain the science about Shadow Slices Ш in Chapter 8 of Part 2:

Shadow Creation

/S/ ubjectivity is illuminated by mirrors. Reflection is the essential process for doing our thinking in /S/. We reflect one association of {idents} off another, and so measure their difference or similarity: good / evil; right / wrong; truth / lies.

We create templates of these {ident} associations, and then use those as reference points. We attach "emotions" to {ident} associations, to make them more powerful. These become our "emotional layers": what we think of as the fundamental elements of our emotional personality.

It's neither easy nor automatic for the 5 Slices to relate in dynamic harmony. All the circumstances of life conspire to de-harmonise, to interfere with the natural "gravity" of our personality.

We can find that the mirroring function doesn't work, or just doesn't seem to work. That perception is probably justified. There's no law of science or nature that says that we must be able to understand our life experiences.

We create understandings: and those are more or less efficient to the circumstances of our life. To maintain <coherence> what we all do is create *Shadow Slices (Ш)*.

A Shadow Slice Ш is an association of {idents} [ideas]
that is unaffected by the dynamics of the Slices.

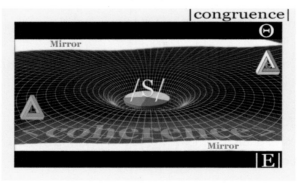

The "impossible triangles" represent Ш Shadow Slices.

Shadow Power

The result is that our <Feelings> and <Thoughts> churn. We feel upset and unbalanced. The Ш sits in our "attic" headspace, as if surrounded by emotional fires and sirens.

Whatever we think and feel, we can't shift the Ш obsession. We are *obsessed.* And possessed by the powerlessness we feel.

The process of attaching "emotions" to thoughts is going on perpetually, every moment of the day. But this is not so with Ш.

Ш appear out of our ordinary efforts to acquire {identation} <coherence> in relation to the unfamiliar: to work out what's going on in our like, and why. We manufacture Ш without positively intending to.

We see also another characteristic: the sense that Ш is part of the fabric of "my" being. "I" cannot let that Ш go, without losing myself: or such part of myself as I sense to be the "real" me.

Ш as Obsession
So, we see the dominance characteristics of Ш:
- separated from "emotional" attachment to thoughts
- outside the gravitational force of Slices on {idents}
- stable in isolation
- mimicking <Constructs>
- acting as a version of <I>
- disconnected from the Anxiety-Soothing Rhythm (ASR)

It's strange that Ш can acquire such seeming dominance in our mind, when they ought to be so fragile. They are disconnected from the ASR: the process which is born into us as our primary survival mechanism, and as our self-teaching system.

These Ш are fragile. That's why we protect them by undermining the normal process in /S/: by suppressing the ASR.

Suppression takes effort. To aid the suppression, we turn to pharmaceuticals and behaviours: processes which can disrupt the ordinary functioning of the ASR.

But that effort takes effort. And we are ultimately fighting a losing battle. We are trying to use artificial measures, to suppress an ASR that is born into us, and which is the electricity for our operating System.

No wonder then that suppression of the ASR symptomises in: lack of energy; listlessness; torpor; depression.

Insomnia is another obvious feature of obsessive Ш. We cannot allow our guard down. We can't let the ASR go about its usual energetic business in /S/. It takes deliberate effort to suppress the ASR. So we sleep fitfully, with one eye open.

There's the picture of Ш obsession: depressed, unidimensional, pouring energy into distraction, yet insomniac and exhausted.

Healing Ш Obsession
Understanding these dynamics provides the key to unlocking Ш obsessions: to release suppression of the ASR.

We can't:
- think our way out of Ш. If we could, they would simply be
- normal {idents}, subject to Slices gravity.
- "feel" our way out of Ш, because that's just another flavour of {identation}.

We can't challenge Ш by using our /S/ubjectivity. All that talk therapy that tries to spin effective Ш challenge out of /S/, is not only wasting everyone's time, it tend to make the problem worse:
- The more you look at Ш, the bigger it gets.
- Trying to ignore Ш, makes it bigger too.

This is how we heal Ш obsession: we simply restore ASR function.

That's really not difficult. The ASR is the motive energy of your entire Self becoming, and has been since the moment of your birth.

We use *Biomorphic* techniques to interrupt ASR suppression. It only takes a few moments. Because the ASR is the life of Self. We simple restore your *Biomorphic Autonomic Balance*

We were engineered to perfection. Shadow Slices are helpless when exposed to the force of unsuppressed ASR. Then our Soothing activates. Instead of Shadow, we find balance, peace and power. This allows us to experience that control, which the Shadow never can: despite all its efforts to try.

Scenario

The Client self-reports an obsession about a person, which is troubling the Client. The Client's problem is usually not so much about what the other person is doing – or not doing – but about the Client's difficulties in dealing with that situation.

Healing

PART 1

Step 1

1.   Sit down for this one.
2.   Go inside your head.
3.   Find that Obsession.

Step 2

1.   You can open or close your eyes as you wish for this next part.

2. Stretch your arms, with open palms: to your left or right side.
3. Feel that Obsession like a rock: a boulder.
4. Feel with your arms and palms like you're trying to push that Obsession away.
5. Like you're trying to push a heavy weight away.
6. Push, really push.
7. Feel that the Obsession won't budge.

Step 3

1. Now, take that boulder of Obsession.
2. Make it small, but as heavy as it can feel to you.
3. Cup your hands.
4. Hold your cupped hands in front of you.
5. Allow the wright of that Obsession boulder to become a super-heavy ball.
6. Hold that super-heavy Obsession ball in your hands.
7. Allow your hands to fall if the weight of that super-heavy Obsession ball forces your hands down.
8. Allow the super-heavy Obsession ball to rest in your hands.
9. Close your hands over it.

Step 4

1. OK, you know where to find the Obsession, any time.
2. Let's keep it there for later.

3.   For now: relax.
4.   Breathe.

PART 2

Step 1

1.   Take the top two fingers of whatever is your
        writing hand.
2.   Place those fingers gently on the waist side
        of your tummy. (You can find the location
        simply by placing your two fingers over your
        belly button, then moving them around to your
        writing hand side).
3.   Rest your fingers at that spot.
4.   Close your eyes.
5.   Breathe normally.

Step 2

1.   Take the top two fingers of your other hand.
2.   Place them gently at the back of your neck, on
        the other side of your body from your other
        fingers. (Location is anywhere between the nape
        of your neck and your collar-bone: just gently
        move your fingers till you find a spot that feels
        fine to you).
3.   Breathe normally.

Step 3: Take 1 to 2 Minutes

1.   Feel a connection between your fingers.
2.   A connection running through your upper body.

Like a wire.

3.   You may feel it hot. You may feel it cold.

4.   If it's a hot connection, allow it to get hotter. If it's a cold connection, allow it to get colder.

5.   Allow the connection to become more intense.

6.   Feel it like the filament in a light bulb, getting brighter as you turn up the voltage.

7.   Allow yourself to allow those toxic energy feelings to run through that connection.

8.   Between your fingers, it feels like angry electric ants scurrying around.

9.   It feels like the connection is becoming barbed wire, spilling toxic chemicals into your body.

10.   Let the angry energy become more intense.

11.   And more. Filling your chest and your head.

Step 4

1.   Now it's coursing through you. That toxic writhing energy.

2.   Take the hand with the fingers which are at your waist.

3.   Take the palm of that hand.

4.   Place it gently over the centre of your chest.

5.   Still feel the angry toxic energy coursing through you.

Step 5

1.   Now, you're going in a few moments to take a huge breath in.

2.   Through your nose or your mouth.

3.   However you'd do it if you were about to jump into a swimming pool.

4.   Big breath in: *Now*.

5.   Hold that breath for 3 long seconds.

6.   One … Two … Three…

7.   Let it out, and at the same time, press your palm into your chest.

8.   You can fall back into your chair, or into a lying position, if you like.

9.   Rest. Breathe normally.

10.   Think whatever thoughts you think. Feel whatever feelings you feel.

PART 3

Step 1

1.   Close your eyes.

2.   Go back to where you were stretching your arms, with open palms.

3.   Now, push at that boulder. Push. Push it away.

4.   Ok: you can't feel anything there.

Step 2

1.   Go back to where you were holding that ball in your hands.

2.   Cup your hands.

3.   Feel for that ball.

4.   That super-heavy Obsession ball.

5.   Ok: you can't feel anything there.

PART 4

Step 1

1.   Go inside your head.
2.   Find the name for that Obsession. Whatever name you give to it.
3.   Just feel whatever feelings you are feeling. Whatever sensations are in your body.
4.   Try and attach any of those feelings, those sensations, to that name.
5.   Relax.
6.   Breathe.

PART 5

Step 1

1.   Go inside your head again.
2.   See a black space, like the inside of a black box.
3.   See if you can see inside that box, without the Obsession being in there.
4.   Put either hand over your chest.
5.   Leave a little gap.
6.   Allow that black space to grow.
7.   Allow any light to come out of it that comes.
8.   Focus on breathing out through that palm
9.   You're breathing in without noticing.
10.   Each time you breathe out, allow that box space to become bigger, and brighter.
11.   As you allow that box space to become bigger, and brighter, breathe out.
12.   Keep going until that black – to – bright box

space fills your whole head.

Step 2
1.   Open your eyes.
2.   Relax.
3.   Maybe stand up and shake out.

End.

Explaining

Part 1 gives you a control – a comparison – for Part 3. In Part 1, you present to your self what we call <coherence> around that Obsession. It's in your mind, and it's in your body. Powerfully, in all of you: just as you find it day by day.

In Part 2, we interrupt your Anxiety repression. Your Anxiety is allowed to burn through you: and to be met by an equal intensity of Soothing.

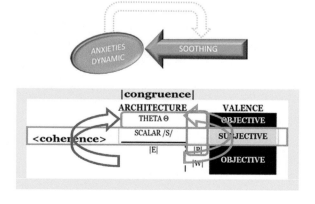

The ASR promotes Biomorphic Autonomic Balance ("BAB"). Now your BAB is restored, you feel calmness: balance.

In Part 3 we take you back to where you used to have <coherence>. But now you can't find the Shadow Slices Ш. This is because your BAB has been restored. You rely on repressing Anxiety to provide you with the power to keep the Ш going.

These Ш are a really heavy drain on power. That's why you feel so sapped of energy all the time: worn out. You have that nervous energy, but it's thin and fragile, and doesn't nourish you.

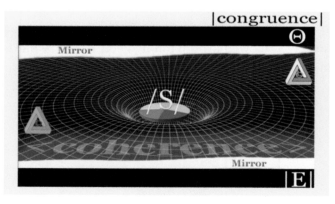

The "impossible triangles" represent Ш Shadow Slices.

The Ш Shadow Slices can't be accessed.

Now, the 5 Slices are re-balancing themselves.

In Part 5, we get you to see just the black, blank box of your mind, cleared of the Ш:

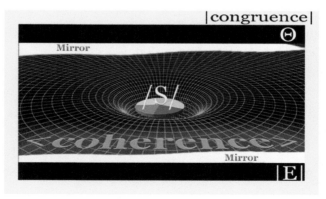

Automatically, your mind snaps back to its Biomorphic Autonomic Balance state. It fills with thoughts and feeling, out of which you create ideas.

Now, there's no artificial interference from Ш.

After Care

There's nothing to stop you re-creating these Shadow Slices Ш. Except you, that is: the normal functioning of your body and mind. These, together, have now been reminded of what life is like without Ш: less misdirected energy; less Anxiety suppression.

Go back into the history of your head, and look at your feelings at the moments:

- you did the breathing out of 3 seconds at Step 9
- the black box turned white light and expanded, at Step 13.

What you felt there, was what you were seeking on the other side of that Obsession: *Closure*. That's the feeling you were looking for. You were trying to find it in the words of behaviour of somebody else: and that would never have come. Because your Obsession can interpret anything any way it likes: and will do whatever it can to keep going.

The real Closure was in those feelings in You, created by You: by your Self as it has known how to struggle for survival since the moment you were born. The most powerful process in your personal world that can ever be.

So, when in the future you want to create Ш Obsession, that weak force will have to reckon with the massive power of the Anxiety-Soothing Cycle, and with your memory of Closure.

So, you will be able to manufacture Ш Obsession: but it's obsession-lite. It's not serious, because you know you can use the Recipe any time: and it's gone.

Now, you can't be fearful of being controlled by Ш, and you can't wish it. So these Ш just become ideas. Good ideas, bad ideas: all just *choices* amongst your thoughts and feelings.

It's not our role to tell you, or even advise you, what to do (or not to do). Our task is to help you to realise your own balance, peace and power. Then you make your decisions.

Nobody can guarantee in advance that - in relation to any

other person who has their own free will - any decision you make will have whatever consequences you intend.

This is what we can guarantee. You are definitely better able to make the best judged decisions and deal with the results, when your own power – not obsessions – inform your thoughts and feelings.

12.   Self-Image

Mirror, mirror on the wall, who's the fairest of them all?

O wad some Pow'r the giftie gie us / To see oursels as ithers see us!

The Evil Queen in *Snow White*, didn't just use the mirror as, well, a mirror. Not just as a vanity device. But as a magic mirror, to tell her if there was anybody fairer than she. Who would then need to be dealt with.

The Scots national poet, Robbie Burns, was looking at a louse on a lady's bonnet in church. Wondering how wonderful it would be if our ability to look at ourselves, could match the realistic views of others.

These two quotes have retained their popular power, over the centuries (*Snow White* 1812; Burns 1786). Because they truly reflect the war of reflection, which casts endless battles in each of our Selfs.

We think that we look in the mirror at ourselves. We don't. We actually create what we "see" in the mirror. It's an act of imagination. Just in the same way that we imagine what others see of us: and we know we do that.

We might think that we can choose our perspectives freely, if we choose to. Let's test that:[5]

Experience: Lens
Setup:
Find a Landscape to look at
Could be a park, or garden
The bigger the vista, the better this *Experience* will work

You can use the image provided if you really have to: but please click the link and bring up the biggest size of it you can.

––––––––––––––

[5] from *Secret Self*, Chapter 2 (2020)

Landscape Image

Step 1:
Relax your gaze upon the image
Notice whatever you notice

Next:

Visualise in your head a Lens
You look through the lens with both eyes.
The lens is clear: it does not distort in any way

It helps to form your forefinger and thumb into a circle,

hold that half an arm's length away and look through that: to give you the sense of the lens visual.

Now:

- take your hand away and put that Lens over one part of the Landscape view (not the whole Landscape)
- focus your visual attention through the Lens

Stop

Discussion:

(1)   You notice that the non-Lens Landscape fades out of view.

(2)   This will be something familiar to anyone who has used spectacles, or binoculars.

So, what does that tell us about paradigm views? Not very much that we didn't already know. Obviously, we can choose not to look through the Lens, and just view the Landscape as we did before the Lens was introduced. Can't we?

Step 2:

Enact the same Setup, with Landscape and Lens.

Next:

Leave the Lens floating there, looking at the Landscape In your mind's eye,
You take position so that you are viewing the Landscape

and Lens, like this:

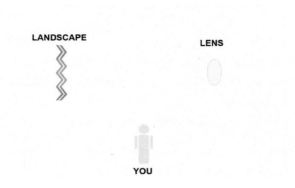

Do it with your own view: don't use this graphic.

Now:

• try viewing through the lens from where you are

Stop
<u>Discussion</u>:
(1)   Now you find that you can't see through the
        Lens

Step 3:
Continue with Setup as per Step 2

And: while holding the presence of Lens in your attention

Now:

• try to view the Landscape

Stop

Discussion:

(1)   You can't really see the Landscape

(2)   You know the Landscape is there, but you can't focus a view on it

(3)   The more you try, the more you feel stuck

(4)   Now you can't see anything

We meet again the rubric:

How we can think governs what we can think.

Being unable to see at all, seems worse than only being able to see from a limited perspective.

What any other individual might think of us isn't real, any more than what we might think of ourselves. It's not real like a rock, or a river is real. Yes, it is a reality for that person, and a reality for us. It's a reality of experience. But that experience is ever-changing.

We've all asked someone "What do you really think of me?" And we've all experienced the hesitation. Not because the other doesn't want to say: but because they really don't know what they think.

The best we or they can do is to think of some abstract ideas: kind; mean; attractive; ugly. Then try to match something in those ideas to something about us.

If this graphic looks familiar:

it should. It's another way of looking at how our minds actually work:

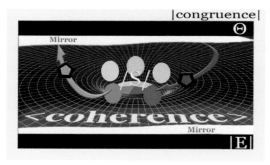

whether alone, or in a crowded street.

We are taking those Mirrors in our minds, and putting versions of them out there, in the world. We spend our entire lives thinking of abstract ideas: then try to match something in those ideas to something about something else.

It's not a useful idea that we get any kind of "truth" out

of any of this. The best we get is: whatever we choose to believe. Our choices are limited by limits on how we can see: as the *Lens Experience* shows.

Scenario

The Client self-reports image problems. The Client may frame this as:

- not liking something about how I see myself
- not liking something about how I believe others see me.

Now, if there are particular *behaviours* which these dislikes refer to, then we are not in the territory of this Chapter. If you go around kicking your dog, then quite reasonably: your dog won't like your kicking; and you shouldn't be feeling great about yourself.

So, that's the first question in this Scenario: *do you think there is anything that you're doing, or deliberately not doing, which relates to these impressions?* If the Client's answer is "Yes", then the Client can work out the solutions for themselves. No Matrixial Healing required.

That's an unusual case. More typically, the Client self-reports feelings of confusion and concern about: *how I see myself / how I believe others see me*.

Healing

PART 1

Step 1

1.   Take a seat.
2.   Close your eyes.
3.   Go inside your head.

Step 2

1.   See yourself now, sitting at home on your sofa.
2.   See yourself thinking whatever thoughts you're thinking. Feeling whatever you're feeling.

Step 3

1.   See yourself looking in a mirror.
2.   You can stand up, in your imagination, if that helps.
3.   You can be clothed – wearing anything – or naked. It's up to you.
4.   See yourself thinking whatever thoughts you're thinking. Feeling whatever you're feeling.

Step 4

1.   Now, you have a visitor.
2.   This is Other You.
3.   It's just you: same age, same time.
4.   Give Other You a handshake or a hug, let them into your room.
5.   Let Other You sit down on the sofa, or on another chair.

Step 5

1. Now, tell Other You what troubling things you're thinking about yourself.
2. Let Other You ask any questions, and make any comments that Other You wants to.
3. You and Other You can spend as long in this conversation as you like.

Step 6

1. Now, show Other You what you can see in the Mirror.
2. Really try to focus on the problems with *how I see myself / how I believe others see me*.
3. Other You totally understands you: is you. Show Other You those problems, in the mirror.

Step 7

1. Time for Other You to go.
2. Other You can come back any time.
3. Say "Bye, thanks for coming" to Other You.

Step 8

1. Open your eyes.
2. Relax.

PART 2

Step 1

1. Take the palm of your writing hand.
2. Place it over your tummy: just where your

tummy button is.

3. Make sure to leave a little gap between your palm and your tummy. This is really important. The gap should be a finger-width.

4. Close your eyes now.

5. Focus on breathing in through the palm of your hand.

6. Feel yourself drawing in breaths, through the palm of your hand.

7. Remember how when you were inside your mummy, that's where your life support came into your body.

8. You can breathe deep or shallow. Slow or fast. Whatever works.

Step 2

1. Your eyes are still closed.

2. Take the palm of your other hand.

3. Place it over your chest.

4. Make sure to leave a little gap between your palm and your chest. This is really important. The gap should be a finger-width.

5. Focus on breathing out through the palm of your hand.

6. Feel yourself pushing out breaths, through the palm of your hand.

End.

Explaining

This is classic Avatar Dialogue Therapy (ADT). We use ADT to bring /S/ back into Autonomic Dynamic Balance (ABD).

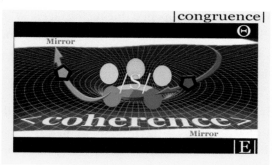

ADT is about getting you to create Mirrors: which we have designed to reflect back {idents} which attach <Affect>, under the gravitational <coherence> of the Slices. This brings you back to ADB.

As we explained in *I Want To Love But*, this Autonomic Dynamic Balance is inherent in every person ever born. It's simply the manifestation in /S/ubjectivity of your Anxiety-Soothing Rhythm.

In ADT:

- rather than getting you to try and think and believe in {thoughts} which are brought to you from "outside";
- we stimulate you to engage with your own <Thoughts>, in {identation} reflection.

A clinical analogy would be to use your own stem cells to rejuvenate mature cells.

After Care
Something strange happened during the Steps. When you got to Step 6, and tried to show Other You those troubling things in the mirror: you couldn't. No matter how hard you tried to look, there was nothing there.

This had an emotional effect. You felt released from the burden of those troubling thoughts. You can still describe the ideas, in words. But now they have the same emotional effect as a telephone directory or shopping list: just words.

The troubles you were experiencing came from fake mirrors. Versions of mirrors that you were making up in your head. A bit like the artificial circle in the *Lens Experience*. Nothing in the world, including you, is actually that in reality. You're just choosing to look at it like that.

By meeting and interacting with Other You, it makes you work with the actual mirrors that you really do have in your head. That's why, when you try to show Other You what's to be seen in the fake mirrors: there's nothing there.

Essentially, you're regaining control over the direction of your thinking. You can't think your way into doing that. All that happens is that you add more power and confusion to the "negative" thoughts. Instead, we straighten the mirrors a bit: so what you see is what you get. That's all you needed.

13.   Communication

Relationships are about communication. So: tell us something we don't know.

All communication is interpretive: at both ends, and in the middle. The way that our thinking - and turning it into words - works is that we can never say what we feel. The best we can do is to try to get more or less close to it. But, our feelings don't "mean" anything, independently of our thoughts about them.

Words and behaviours are "out there". They are in the world, independent of each of us. But only an individual's thoughts give meaning to such things. What I think I am doing, and what you think about what I do, are two completely different things.

Relationship therapy, and practical common sense, tells us that communicating with each other is better than not communicating. Well, that depends on what we're each trying to communicate, and how each of us can, or chooses to, understand it.

We're describing, not criticising. This is just one of the how-things-are about being human.

Scenario

Client (or Clients) self-report a sense of wanting to be able to feel closer to each other.

Silent Healing

PART 1

Step 1

1.   Sit down for this.
2.   You can keep your eyes open.

Step 2

1.   Take the palm of your writing hand.
2.   Move it over your thigh.
3.   About a hand's breadth above your thigh.
4.   Now, close your eyes.
5.   Feel whatever you feel.

Step 3

1.   Now, move that hand over your tummy.
2.   About a hand's breadth away from your clothes.
3.   Feel whatever you feel.

Step 4

1.   Now, move that hand over your chest.
2.   About a hand's breadth away from your clothes.
3.   Feel whatever you feel.

Step 5

1.   Now, move that hand back over your tummy.

2.   About a hand's breadth away from your clothes.

3.   Feel the difference you feel.

Step 6

1.   Now, move that hand back over your thigh.

2.   About a hand's breadth away from your clothes.

3.   Feel the difference you feel.

Step 7

1.   Take your hand away.

2.   Open your eyes.

3.   Relax.

End.

PART 2

Step 1

1.   You and your partner sit down for this.

2.   You can keep your eyes open.

Step 2

1.   Follow steps 2 to 10 with each other.

2.   Try to do it the same time.

3.   So your hand is hovering over their thigh; and they with you.

4.   And so on

5.   Take as long as you like.

End.

Explaining
In Part 1, you met your own energy. There's nothing to think. Nothing to feel. It just seems: nice.

There's nothing you can think or feel or do to change that energy. Well, technically, there is and it changes all the time. But for present purposes, that energy is what it is. You just sense it.

In Part 2, you share that sense with somebody else. There are no words, no behaviours getting in the way. All that can get in the way is someone's refusals to open up to sensing that energy. If that's happening, it provides a stepping-off point for talking about that. But now we really are getting somewhere: if you can't (or choose not to) feel my body's simple organic energy, then that's not my fault. It can't be.

It's not your fault either. It's not your intention to block that energy. Try it alone, with just yourself. Then, have a go with me. Now it works. Now we're communicating: no words, no behaviours.

After Care
This might seem so ridiculously simple. It is. And it's the simplicity that makes it capable of being so meaningful. We get to understand that we can feel each other: sense each other.

Yes, of course, we could energy-touch anyone on the planet.

But we are *choosing* to make it happen with each other.

The problem with touching – skin contact – lovely though it can be, is that it can set off all sorts of thoughts and feelings. Energy-touching doesn't. It conveys balance, peace and power. Perfect communication: without words or behaviour.

Other You

In this Healing, we're going to use your Avatar. This is "Other You". Now, this is different to the *You2* concept. You don't need to close your eyes, and make a connection: and so on.

You're just imagining yourself being there. Same age, same you. This is really easy. We do it all the time. We run scenarios in our head where an imaginary "me" does things. Imagining getting up to make a cup of tea. Thinking about crossing the road. The key thing is that the Other You is just you: right as you are, right now.

Avatar Healing

PART 1

Step 1

1.   Take a seat.
2.   Close your eyes.
3.   Go inside your head.

Step 2

1.   See yourself now, sitting at home on your sofa.

2.   See yourself thinking whatever thoughts you're thinking. Feeling whatever you're feeling.

Step 3

1.   See yourself looking in a mirror frame.
2.   You can stand up, in your imagination, if that helps.
3.   You can be clothed – wearing anything – or naked. It's up to you.
4.   Looking back at you, from inside that mirror frame, is: Your Partner.
5.   See Your Partner looking back at you from in side that mirror frame.
6.   See yourself thinking whatever thoughts you're thinking. Feeling whatever you're feeling.
7.   See yourself reacting to what Your Partner is thinking, or feeling, or saying, or doing.

Step 4

1.   Now, you have a visitor.
2.   This is Other You.
3.   It's just you: same age, same time.
4.   Give Other You a handshake or a hug, let them into your room.
5.   Let Other You sit down on the sofa, or on another chair.

Step 5

1.   Now, tell Other You what troubling things

you're thinking about yourself.

2. Let Other You ask any questions, and make any comments that Other You wants to.

3. You and Other You can spend as long in this conversation as you like.

Step 6

1. Now, show Other You the mirror frame.

2. Show Other You what Your Partner is thinking, or feeling, or saying, or doing.

3. Really try to focus on any problems with *how I see myself / how I believe another sees me.*

4. Other You totally understands you: is you. Show Other You those problems, in the mirror.

Step 7

1. Time for Other You to go.

2. Other You can come back any time.

3. Say "Bye, thank for coming" to Other You.

Step 8

1. Open your eyes.

2. Relax.

PART 2

Step 1

1. Take the palm of your writing hand.

2. Place it over your tummy: just where your tummy button is.

3.   Make sure to leave a little gap between your
        palm and your tummy. This is really important.
        The gap should be a finger-width.
4.   Close your eyes now.
5.   Focus on breathing in through the palm of your
        hand.
6.   Feel yourself drawing in breaths, through the
        palm of your hand.
7.   Remember how when you were inside your
        mummy, that's where your life support
        came into your body.
8.   You can breathe deep or shallow. Slow or fast.
        Whatever works.

Step 2

1.   Your eyes are still closed.
2.   Take the palm of your other hand.
3.   Place it over your chest.
4.   Make sure to leave a little gap between your
        palm and your chest. This is really important.
        The gap should be a finger-width.
5.   Focus on breathing out through the palm of
        your hand.
6.   Feel yourself pushing out breaths, through the
        palm of your hand.

                        End.

Explaining
You'll recognise this as the same *Healing* as in the last

Chapter, with a twist. Now, you're focusing on the "negative self-image" stuff you believe is coming from Your Partner, to you.

After Care
With your emotional release from the burden of all that, it allows you to just be in Your Partner's own reality: if that's where you want to be. If you don't, then you're not really into having a relationship with that individual at all.

Your de-coupling from the emotional baggage train, allows you to just ask what Your Partner thinks: about whatever you want to know about.

We can't change the rules of being a Self: *how we can think determines what we can think*. But we can use this Recipe, to allow the fullest freedom in *how we can think*: rather than binding it with unhelpful distortions.

Results are not guaranteed. Making better use of opportunities is.

CHAPTER 5

SYMPTOMATIC RELIEF

Our bodies produce symptoms, when responding to challenges. It's a difficult balancing act for our physical systems. Too much symptomatic action can be enough to kill us. This is the problem with the "cytokine storm" seen in Covid and other causes: where the initial infection produces a chain-reaction of response. It's not the Covid that kills: it's the immune response, killing off both healthy and infected cells.

Less dramatically, viral infection symptoms can interfere with our lives to such an extent that they compromise well-being: by stopping us doing things that we really need to do; and by so using up our energy resources that the infection drags on longer than necessary.

In this Chapter, we look at *Healing* Recipes for 3 symptomatic conditions: viral; neurological and compound. There's much in these *Healing* techniques that we can apply to other conditions.

We need to stress, when dealing with clinical conditions such as these, that you should always seek appropriate clinical diagnosis, advice and treatment from a recognised medical physician.

These Recipes are not intended for use in acute cases: that is, cases requiring hospital treatment. The landscape for these Recipes, is where you can just about cope, but you'd like to improve your coping experience.

14.   Covid Symptoms

Every reader will be familiar with the well-known list of Covid symptoms:[6]
The main symptoms of coronavirus are:

- **a high temperature** – this means you feel hot to touch on your chest or back (you do not need to measure your temperature)
- **a new, continuous cough** – this means coughing a lot for more than an hour, or 3 or more coughing episodes in 24 hours (if you usually have a cough, it may be worse than usual)
- **a loss or change to your sense of smell or taste** – this means you've noticed you cannot smell or taste anything, or things smell or taste different to normal

Most people with coronavirus have at least 1 of these symptoms.

Obviously, these symptoms overlap with influenza symptoms, which is why testing is needed to tell the difference.

Scenario

Client self-reports one or more of these symptoms. Some Clients have tested positive for Covid.

Client's condition is non-acute. We always advise that if symptoms do worsen, or the Client has any other concerns, to contact an appropriately qualified physician.

---

[6] https://www.nhs.uk/conditions/coronavirus-covid-19/symptoms/

Healing

Step 1

1.   You can sit down, or stand. Whatever works for
        you.
2.   Close your eyes.
3.   Go inside your head.
4.   Find where the symptom pain is worst: maybe
        your throat, or chest, or wherever.

Step 2

1.   Take the top 2 fingers of your writing hand.
2.   Place them gently on your body, at that worst
        pain place.

Step 3

1.   Feel a connection, in your head, with Second
        You: You$_2$.
2.   This is just you: yourself, looking at you.
3.   You$_2$ is just by your shoulder.
4.   Allow You$_2$'s head to connect with yours.

Step 4

1.   Allow You$_2$ to see where the pain is: as shown by
        your 2 fingers.
2.   Allow You$_2$ to feel the pain.

Step 5

1.   Feel that connection, like a thread, between
        You$_2$'s head and that place of pain.

2.   Now, allow that pain to begin to move along
        that thread, to You$_2$.

3.   You can imagine the pain being carried in
        carriages of a train, along the thread, to You$_2$.

Step 6

1.   You may feel some resistance. That's normal.

2.   Ordinary You needs to take a step back.

3.   Think of ordinary You as being able to take a
        tiny step back outside yourself: like a ghost or a
        spirit.

4.   Just let that ghost or spirit take a tiny step back
        out of yourself.

Step 7

1.   Feel that connection, like a thread, between
        You$_2$'s head and that place of pain.

2.   Allow that pain to begin to move along that
        thread, to You$_2$.

3.   It's moving much easier now.

4.   Keep it going.

Step 8

1.   OK: relax

2.   Open your eyes.

3.   Breathe.

End.

Explaining

This is Congruence Interface Therapy (CIT), which is a branch of *Psychotectics*.

These You2 Avatar techniques are used in *CIT Morphonics*. We help you to turn on a connection with (sort of) computer programs operating between the Electromagnetic cloud in your brain and the parts of your brain that control things like your breathing.

Together, these can influence how your body responds symptomatically to viral infection.

One way of thinking about this (though it's not scientifically correct), is that our symptoms-control centre brain is part of a virtual reality spacesuit. By adjusting the settings on the spacesuit, that changes how we manage our symptoms.

Connecting with the EM cloud "computer program", alters the "spacesuit" settings. We use the *You2 Avatar* as a way of getting the Client to connect the /S/ubjective layer of mind, with the "computer program" layer of the spacesuit.

After Care

The reduction in flu-like symptoms (nose, throat, eye soreness) typically happens instantly, during the *Healing*.

Clients who have tested positive for Covid, and have the classic loss of taste and smell, report that they wake up the next morning with those functions restored. It takes that little bit longer for these "spacesuit" settings to adjust.

We find in Practice, that the symptoms relief is permanent.

15.   Headache

There can be many reasons for experiencing a headache.

Sometimes, you're just running "too hot", like after an argument. You probably wouldn't seek *Healing* for that. You understand that your blood has been pumping overtime, your systems have become overwhelmed, resulting in headache. Just calm down and it should go away.

It does feel like a problem in need of *Healing*, when you keep getting headaches every few days (or more frequently), and for no obvious reason.

You should always seek advice from an appropriately qualified physician. Such headaches could, in some cases, be symptomatic of a tumour, or other serious neurophysical illness.

Scenario
For now, let's focus on the otherwise healthy Client, who is suffering headaches, for no apparent reason.

15A   Biomorphic Healing

Step 1

1.   Take the palm of your writing hand.
2.   Place it over your tummy: just where your
        tummy button is.
3.   Make sure to leave a little gap between your
        palm and your tummy. This is really important.
        The gap should be a finger-width.
4.   Close your eyes now.
5.   Focus on breathing in through the palm of your
        hand.
6.   Feel yourself drawing in breaths, through the
        palm of your hand.
7.   Remember how when you were inside your
        mummy, that's where your life support
        came into your body.
8.   You can breathe deep or shallow. Slow or fast.
        Whatever works.

Step 2

1.   Your eyes are still closed.
2.   Take the palm of your other hand.
3.   Place it over your chest.
4.   Make sure to leave a little gap between your
        palm and your chest. This is really important.
        The gap should be a finger-width.
5.   Focus on breathing out through the palm of
        your hand.

6.   Feel yourself pushing out breaths, through the palm of your hand.

End.

Explaining
We call these Steps *Angel Wings*. We are giving your Self system a reset.

You will feel your head clearing, your thoughts like dancers on a crowded dancefloor, moving to the sides as the band stops playing.

Typically, you'll feel resistance to that: like you're trying to keep the thought-dancers in your head, even without the music.

So, we'll apply another Recipe, to help with this reset resistance.

15B   Psychotectic Healing
Step 1
1.   You can sit down, or stand. Whatever works for you.
2.   Close your eyes.

Step 2
1.   Take the top 2 fingers of your writing hand.
2.   Place them gently on the back of your neck.

Step 3

1.   Feel a connection, in your head, with Second
        You: You2.

2.   This is just you: yourself, looking at you.

3.   You2 is just by your shoulder.

4.   Allow You2's head to connect with yours.

Step 4

1.   Go into You2's head

2.   Look inside You2's head to see where the head
        ache pain is.

3.   See if you can feel any pain or tension in You2's
neck.

Step 5

1.   Take control of You2's head.

2.   Use that control to clear You2's head.

3.   Just use your power to allow You2's head to feel
        calm and clear.

Step 6

1.   OK: relax

2.   Open your eyes.

3.   Breathe.

                        End.

Explaining

This is Congruence Interface Therapy (CIT), which is a
branch of *Psychotectics*. These You2 Avatar techniques are

used in *CIT Morphonics*.

We are helping to clear interference from the connection between your (sort of) computer programs operating between the Electromagnetic cloud in your brain, and other parts of your brain.

Something is going wrong with those connections. Your "computer" brain can run a diagnostic and find out what that is. Then fix it.

You know how when you take a modern car into a garage and they hook up its computer to an iPad. Then run a diagnostic. Then use software to alter the way the car is running. That's kind of what we're doing here.

We just needed to get your "thoughts and feelings" head out of the way for a few moments.

After Care
Now, you'll be feeling clearer in your head, but still a little unbalanced.

So please do *Angel Wings* again. This time, you'll find that much easier. You'll feel no or low resistance to that breathing. The music has been turned off now, or gone very quiet. The thought-dancers in your head will be moving to the side of your head, clearing that space.

You can repeat this Recipe, whenever you have a headache. To help you not to get headaches at all, or only at low level, try to do *Angel Wings* a few times a week. It only takes a minute or so.

16.   *Fibromyalgia*

The NHS information says:[7]

> Fibromyalgia, also called fibromyalgia syndrome (FMS), is a long-term condition that causes pain all over the body.
>
> **Symptoms of fibromyalgia**
> As well as widespread pain, people with fibromyalgia may also have:
> - increased sensitivity to pain
> - extreme tiredness (fatigue)
> - muscle stiffness
> - difficulty sleeping
> - problems with mental processes (known as "fibro-fog"), such as problems with memory and concentration
> - *headaches*
> - *irritable bowel syndrome (IBS)*, a digestive condition that causes stomach pain and bloating
>
> If you think you have fibromyalgia, visit a GP. Treatment is available to ease some of its symptoms, although they're unlikely to disappear completely.
>
> **How fibromyalgia is treated**
> Although there's currently no cure for fibromyalgia, there are treatments to help relieve some of the symptoms and make the condition easier to live with. Treatment tends to be a combination of:

---

[7] https://www.nhs.uk/conditions/fibromyalgia/

- medicine, such as *antidepressants* and painkillers
- talking therapies, such as *cognitive behavioural therapy (CBT)* and *counselling*
- lifestyle changes, such as exercise programmes and relaxation techniques

Exercise in particular has been found to have a number of important benefits for people with fibromyalgia, including helping to reduce pain.

What causes fibromyalgia?

The exact cause of fibromyalgia is unknown, but it's thought to be related to abnormal levels of certain chemicals in the brain and changes in the way the central nervous system (the brain, spinal cord and nerves) processes pain messages carried around the body.

It's also suggested that some people are more likely to develop fibromyalgia because of genes inherited from their parents.

In many cases, the condition appears to be triggered by a physically or emotionally stressful event, such as:

- an injury or infection
- giving birth
- having an operation
- the breakdown of a relationship
- the death of a loved one

Who's affected?

Anyone can develop fibromyalgia, although it affects around 7 times as many women as men.

The condition typically develops between the ages of 30 and 50, but can occur in people of any age, including children and the elderly.

It's not clear exactly how many people are affected by fibromyalgia, although research has suggested it could be a relatively common condition. Some estimates suggest nearly 1 in 20 people may be affected by fibromyalgia to some degree.

One of the main reasons it's not clear how many people are affected is because fibromyalgia can be a difficult condition to diagnose. There's no specific test for the condition, and the symptoms can be similar to a number of other conditions.

Support groups
Many people with fibromyalgia find that support groups provide an important network where they can talk to others living with the condition.
Fibromyalgia Action UK is a charity that offers information and support to people with fibromyalgia.
If you have any questions about fibromyalgia, call the charity's helpline on 0300 999 3333.
The charity also has a network of local *support groups* you may find helpful and an *online community*, where you can find out about news, events and ongoing research into the condition.

Another support group you may find useful is *UK Fibromyalgia*.

To me, 'Fibro' clearly involves a feedback problem. For example, something causes a change in our digestive system. That stops us getting energy efficiently out of food. This then reduces the operating efficiency of our body. That leads to problems with brain function. Those problems then complicate our digestive system.

Matrixial Therapy Techniques are well-developed for Fibro problems. We get the "computer" brain to scan and analyse body function problems and provide solutions. This puts in place automated repair systems, which can then start to undo the continuous harm being done by the "bad feedback".

NHS guidance and our own Matrixial theory and practice observation agree that Fibro involves layers of problems. In this section, we're going to focus on just one aspect of Fibro healing. Other Recipes can be used in combination. Each gets at a specific layer of problem.

We often say that Fibro is like having a pile of baths, all overflowing with pain water. The path to recovery begins with lowering the level of pain water in one bath. Just achieving this, brings the Client insight and confidence that the same can be achieved with the other bath waters. This actually kick-starts that very process.

This is what we are looking to do. To get the "computer" brain to automate recovery and repair cycles, which will reverse the disrepair cycle that Fibro actually is.

Scenario

The Client self-reports with Fibro. There is usually a leading aspect: a pain or problem which the Client feels most often and most intensely.

For muscular, nerve and joint pain, please refer to the Recipes in Chapter 6.

Here we will focus on healing the digestion cycle.

Gastric Healing

The Client should begin any healing session with *Angel Wings*. This allows a base level balance, before using another Recipe.

Step 1

1.   You can sit down, or stand. Whatever works for you.
2.   Close your eyes.

Step 2

1.   Reach out your writing hand arm.
2.   Feel a connection, in your head, with Second You: You2.
3.   This is just you: yourself, looking at you.
4.   You2 is at the end of your arm, being touched by your hand.
5.   Allow You2's head to connect with yours.

Step 3

1.   Go into You2's head
2.   Look inside You2's head to see where the stomach discomfort is.

Step 4

1.   Use your hand to stroke You2's stomach.
2.   Feel the power in your hand (a tingling in your fingers, a warmth in your hand).
3.   Pass that energy into You2.

Step 5

1. You may feel resistance: like the energy doesn't want to leave you.
2. Allow You2 to look inside you.
3. Feel the connection with You2's head.
4. Feel You2 looking inside you.
5. Feel that connection.

Step 6

1. Again, use your hand to stroke You2's stomach.
2. Feel the power in your hand (a tingling in your fingers, a warmth in your hand).
3. Pass that energy into You2.
4. Now, you can feel that positive energy running the length of the body of You2.
5. Keep feeding that energy, while it feels nice.
6. Until You2 feels "full up".

Step 7

1. OK: relax
2. Open your eyes.
3. Breathe.

End.

Explaining

Immediately, you can feel a balance, peace and power in your own stomach area. Your digestive tract, from your mouth down to your stomach feels clear.

You will be feeling a warmth, spreading from your stomach. You may be feeling a releasing of tension in your lower spine.

Some Clients will start feeling hungry straight away. Go eat! And enjoy.

After Care
The Client can repeat this You2 connection experience, any time. The Client should activate their You2 connection, just before every meal, as they sit down to eat.

Just take a few seconds, to switch on that You2 connection. Immediately, the Client will feel their tummy settle, ready for food. Feeling that, will reduce the stress around food. The Client will produce endorphins – happy brain chemicals – which will help digestion, and which will allow the food to taste and feel better. We are turning a negative feedback cycle into a series of positive, life-enhancing experiences.

17. Skin Blotches

You can develop patches of skin which are uneven in colour, compared to the rest of your skin. This is distinct from Psoriasis, where patches of skin develop a crusting: for guidance, see https://www.nhs.uk/conditions/psoriasis/.

Your skin is a complex biosystem. Essential components,

apart from the skin cells, and layers of cells underneath, are the nerve and blood vessels which "feed" the cells.

Common varieties of skin disorders include: [8]

Tinea Versicolor can appear as white spots or spots in shades of pink, red, and brown. They're more noticeable on tanned skin and may get larger over time.

Other symptoms include:

- itching
- scaling
- dryness

Everyone has microscopic yeast living on their skin, but people with tinea versicolor experience an overgrowth of the yeast. It isn't clear why it happens, but it may be caused by:

- excessive sweating
- oily skin
- humid, warm conditions
- a weakened immune system

Tinea versicolor most commonly occurs in people living in tropical climates. It can affect people in any ethnic group. Teenagers may be more susceptible than people in other age groups due to their more oily skin.

Treatment options

Symptoms usually go away in cooler weather, but they may reappear when the temperature and humidity climb. Treating the disorder in its earliest stages may help break this cycle.

If your symptoms are mild, you can try treating them at home with over-the-counter (OTC) antifungal products. Antifungals help reduce yeast,

---

[8] https://www.healthline.com/health/skin-disorders/white-spots-on-skin#lichen-sclerosus

eliminating or lessening the spots. Topical medications include:

- miconazole
- selenium sulfide
- ketoconazole
- clotrimazole

Depending on how severe your symptoms are, it may be weeks or months before the spots fade. Often, the skin regains its former appearance.

If home treatments aren't enough, a dermatologist can prescribe stronger topical creams or an oral medication. You may need to repeat these treatments periodically.

Eczema (atopic dermatitis) is characterized by red, itchy rashes with raised bumps. These rashes may include white spots or patches. Commonly affected areas include:

- face
- scalp
- hands
- feet
- elbows
- eyelids
- wrists
- backs of the knees

The rash almost always itches, sometimes intensely and especially at night. If scratched, the rash can lead to open, leaky sores. Over time, areas of the body most affected by eczema may become thickened, dry, and scaly.

Eczema rashes may flare up and recede without an obvious pattern. Symptoms may even remain dormant for years at a time.

Eczema is common in children but can affect people of any age. It may be a lifelong condition. It commonly begins before age five, and may even start during infancy. It's also common in people who have allergies, such as hay fever.

162

Treatment options

Treatment for eczema focuses on symptom management. You may be able to reduce your symptoms with proactive behaviours that keep your skin healthy and lubricated.

Try these tips:
- Use mild cleansers instead of harsh soaps.
- Treat the rash with medicated creams.
- Keep your skin moisturised.
- Avoid overly long and hot showers or baths.
- Wear gloves when using cleaning solvents.
- Use all-natural solvents instead of chemicals.
- Avoid allergens in the environment.
- Avoid air pollution, including cigarette smoke.

Using anti-itch creams or an oral allergy medication, such as an antihistamine, may help reduce itching.

Vitilogo occurs when certain skin cells called melanocytes stop making melanin. Melanin is the pigment that gives colour to your skin, hair, and eyes. Without pigment, white patches form.

These patches can appear anywhere on the body. Vitiligo is usually symmetric, though it can appear on only one side of the body. Typical areas affected by vitiligo include the knees, hands, genitals, and hair. It can also affect areas with mucous membranes, such as the inside of the mouth and nose.

Vitiligo typically develops in your twenties, but it can occur at any age. Its cause is currently unknown. Vitiligo may be connected to genetics or autoimmune diseases, such as hyperthyroidism.

Treatment options

Treatment for vitiligo is cosmetic and aims to restore colour to the affected skin. It can take trial and error with several therapies. Your doctor may recommend one or more of the following:

163

- steroids
- immunomodulators
- ultraviolet light therapy

Some people with vitiligo find that using cover-up cosmetics is their most effective option for reducing the appearance of white patches.
In severe cases, surgical treatments may also be an option. Your doctor can talk to you about what may be right for you

Idiopathic guttate hypomelanosis (IGH) aka 'sun spots' manifests as small white spots on skin that receives high amounts of sun exposure. This includes areas such as arms and legs. The white spots are painless and benign.

IGH is more common in people with light skin and may appear in women at younger ages than it does in men. However, it usually affects women older than 40.

Treatment options
Wearing sunscreen and avoiding excessive sun exposure is a good first step toward reducing further skin damage. Only a few options exist for treating sun spots after they appear. If you want to reduce the appearance of these white spots, talk to your doctor about calcineurin inhibitors or laser treatments.

Pityriasis alba typically starts out as pink, slightly scaly plaques on the chin and cheeks. They may be round, oval, or irregular in shape, and are usually dry and scaly to the touch. The patches may clear up on their own or fade to white over time.
The skin disorder is most commonly found in children and teens. It's also more likely to occur in people with dark skin. Pityriasis alba is likely related to eczema.

Treatment options
Pityriasis usually clears up on its own, but recurrences can happen. Treatments used to diminish the white patches include moisturizing creams, topical steroids, or nonsteroidal creams.

Scenario

Client who is otherwise in reasonable good health complains of white patches. Usually small and spread out. On arms, legs, upper chest.

Healing

Step 1

1.   You can sit down, or stand. Whatever works for you.
2.   Close your eyes.

Step 2

1.   Take the top 2 fingers of your writing hand.
2.   Place them gently at one of the patch places.

Step 3

1.   Feel a connection, in your head, with Second You: You_2.
2.   This is just you: yourself, looking at you.
3. You_2 is just by your shoulder.
4.   Allow You_2's head to connect with yours.

Step 4

1.   Allow You_2 to see where your skin problem places are.
2.   Take your time, and see those places through You_2's head.

Step 5

1.   Ordinary You needs to take a step back.
2.   Just let that ghost or spirit take a tiny step back out of yourself.
3.   Think of ordinary You as being able to take a tiny step back outside yourself: like a ghost or a spirit. To become Step-Out you.

Step 6

1.   Allow Step-Out you to see the same skin problem places on the body of You$_2$.
2.   See those problem places on the outside of You$_2$'s body.
3.   Now allow Step-Out you to go inside You$_2$'s body.
4.   See those problem places on the inside of You$_2$'s body

Step 7

1.   Allow You$_2$ to give to those problem places the nerve movement, the blood flow, whatever else it needs.
2.   Just allow that flow of nourishing health to those problem places inside You$_2$.
3.   As you do this, you will feel, in your own body, a warmth glowing around those problem places. If the problem places are on your arms, you'll feel your fingertips tingling.
      If the problem places are on your legs, you'll feel your toes tingling.

If the problem places are on your chest, you'll feel your neck tingling.

Step 8

1.   OK: relax
2.   Open your eyes.
3.   Breathe.

End.

Explaining

We helped to create a mirror version of you. A bit like taking a scan and looking at the readout. We then allowed your "computer" brain to scan the readout and diagnose what the problems are.

As soon as your "computer" brain could see the problems, it gave instructions for them to get fixed. That's why you feel the warmth and tingling. The control system for your body is finding and fixing the problems.

After Care

You'll feel a tingling and warmth in the affected place. After a while, you'll notice nerves that come off your spinal cord pumping. This is good. It means that your body is recognising that the site of your skin issue needs supplying with good things which your body produces.

You may see a difference immediately, usually a change in your skin tone around the affected area. What was a sharp line between the affected area and outside, becomes fuzzy.

You should expect positive changes over the next few days. There's no point repeating the Recipe during this time. Now that your body and brain can "see" the problem, they will work together to fix it.

CHAPTER 6

INJURY RELIEF

The mind-body relationship has been discussed in medicine and philosophy for over two thousand years. The general view of Western medicine is that the mind has no-to-low influence over the body. That you certainly can't just think yourself better.

Matrixial Science agrees with that last bit. Our thinking and feeling minds are incredible at creation. They are rubbish at diagnosis – of our Selfs.

Alternative and complementary healing takes a more "holistic" view. Much of what they say seems logical. Clearly, what they do can work for some people: otherwise these practices would have died out long ago. But there's a distinct reliance on charismatic healers, with special powers. All of which tends to lead to higher power ideas.

Now, you're the boss of you: always. You can choose what you wish to believe. Matrixial Healing isn't about believing anything. It's just about doing: following the Steps in the Recipes. These clearly work. Matrixial Science tells us why they work: because of the processes which happen in the Systems Architecture of the Self. It's just as clinical, and material evidence based, as pills and potions.

The Recipes dealing with injury relief are quite "zap-pow". Instant results, with long term relief. Because it's all about healing physical symptoms, you get a real buzz from seeing and feeling the *Healing* work. Your mind might trick you, but your pains – and pain relief - don't.

18.   Sports Injuries

In this Scenario, we're looking at mild – but painful – sports injuries. A muscle strain from the gym. A twist or mild sprain from some other sport.

We're not dealing here with bone breaks, or any injury which has broken the skin. That needs clinical repair.

Scenario

The Client self-reports a mild injury. Say a forearm, or calf, which feels painful after activity.

Healing

Step 1

1.   You can sit down, or stand. Whatever works for you.

2.   Take the top 2 fingers of your writing hand. If that hand/arm is injured, you can use your other hand.

3.   Place them gently on your body, at the worst pain place.

Step 2

1.   Now, close your eyes.
2.   Feel a connection, in your head, with Second
        You: You₂.
3.   This is just you: yourself, looking at you.
4.   You₂ is just by your shoulder.
5.   Allow You₂'s head to connect with yours.

Step 3

1.   Allow You₂ to see where the pain is: as shown by
        your 2 fingers.
2.   Allow You₂ to feel the pain.

Step 4

1.   Feel that connection, like a thread, between
        You₂'s head and that place of pain.
2.   Now, allow that pain to begin to move along
        that thread, to You₂.
3.   You can imagine the pain being carried in
        carriages of a train, along the thread, to You₂.

Step 5

1.   You may feel some resistance. That's normal.
2.   Ordinary You needs to take a step back.
3.   Think of ordinary You as being able to take a
        tiny step back outside yourself: like a ghost or a
        spirit.
4.   Just let that ghost or spirit take a tiny step back
        out of yourself.

Step 6

1.   Feel that connection, like a thread, between You2's head and that place of pain.

2.   Allow that pain to begin to move along that thread, to You2.

3.   It's moving much easier now.

4.   Keep it going.

Step 7

1.   OK: relax

2.   Open your eyes.

3.   Breathe.

End.

Explaining

This is Congruence Interface Therapy (CIT), which is a branch of *Psychotectics*.

These You2 Avatar techniques are used in *CIT Morphonics*. We help you to turn on a connection with (sort of) computer programs operating between the Electromagnetic cloud in your brain, and the parts of your brain which control things like your breathing.

Together, these can influence how your body responds symptomatically to injury.

Essentially, it is your nerves that are communicating pain

signals from the injury site to your brain. That's fine. The problem is that your ordinary thinking brain is reacting, and getting in the way. It's kind of panicking. Sending more signals back down those nerve pathways, and causing trouble at the other end.

So we get your "computer" brain to get directly involved. It works out what's really needed – if anything. This interruption of your thinking brain allows it to go back to what it's actually good it.

After Care
We find in Practice, that the relief is permanent.

Use the *Angel Wings* Recipe, to help bring you balance, peace and power.

19.   Rapid Healing

Here, we are dealing with bumps and bruises. These can be mildly painful, or irritating.

Scenario
The Client self-reports, and can even show us, a bruise (maybe more than one) or bump.

Healing
Step 1
1.   You can sit down, or stand. Whatever works for you.
2.   Take the palm of your writing hand.

3.   Hover it over the bruise or bump place.

Step 2

1.   Now, close your eyes.
2.   Feel the energy coming off your body at that spot.
3.   Move your hand to hover somewhere else over your body.
4.   Feel the difference in energy.
5.   Hover your hand back to over the bruise or bump place.

Step 3

1.   Feel a connection, in your head, with Second You: You$_2$.
2.   This is just you: yourself, looking at you.
3.   You$_2$ is just by your shoulder.
4.   Allow You$_2$'s head to connect with yours.

Step 4

1.   You're going to move your hover hand, like it's hovering over You$_2$'s body.
2.   First, move your hand to hover somewhere else over your body: *and feel yourself doing that with You$_2$'s body.*
3.   Now, hover your hand back to over the bruise or bump place: *and feel yourself doing that with You$_2$'s body.*

Step 5

1.   You may feel some resistance now feeling the energy. That's normal.
2.   Ordinary You needs to take a step back.
3.   Think of ordinary You as being able to take a tiny step back outside yourself: like a ghost or a spirit.
4.   Just let that ghost or spirit take a tiny step back out of yourself.

Step 6

1.   Feel that connection, like a thread, between You2's head and that place of pain.
2.   Again, move your hand to hover somewhere else over your body: *and feel yourself doing that with You2's body.*
3.   Now, hover your hand back to over the bruise or bump place: *and feel yourself doing that with You2's body.*
4.   The energy is flowing much easier now.
5.   Keep it going.

Step 7

1.   OK: relax
2.   Open your eyes.
3.   Breathe.

End.

Explaining

This is *Morphonics*, within Congruence Interface Therapy (CIT), which is a branch of *Psychotectics*.

Here, we're using that organic cell energy, running through your whole body, that we met in Part 4. We're connecting the routing of that energy (which runs with your nerves) to your "computer" brain.

Like hooking up your modern car to a diagnostic run off an iPad. Rather than letting loose your amateur car-mechanic-thinking Self, to tinker around with the operating systems.

After Care

You'll see the results here over a day or so. Cellular regeneration takes time. But it's much quicker than you trying to think your way to being better.

20. Spinal Neuropathy

Pretty much everyone's spine is a mess, beyond a certain age at least. It's an anatomical legacy of how we fit together, it seems. Pressure being placed on the spinal vertebrae 24 hours a day, even during sleep.

The symptoms can range from mild, but irritating ache, to "need to lie on the floor and die" slipped (or bulging) disc. In any of these cases you should consult an appropriate clinical physician.

Where *Matrixial Healing* can help, is in dealing with the spinal neuropathy: the nerve sensations that communicate the pain from the symptomizing places to the brain. We can interrupt that transmission. You still need to get the physical problem fixed: but you'll feel less discomfort while doing that.

Scenario

The Client self-reports nerve pain coming from the spine. This could be: in the spine itself; from a slipped or herniated disc; and also radiating into arms or legs, from the spine.

Healing

PART 1

Step 1

1.   Lie down.
2.   On a sofa or bed, but if you can stand it, even better on a carpeted floor.

Step 2

1.   Take the palm of your writing hand.
2.   Hover it over your body: a hand's breadth from your clothes. Try to match the position to where in your spine the pain is worst.

Step 3

1.   Take the top 2 fingers of your other hand.
2.   Place them gently on the back of your neck. At

the side of your body where your writing hand fingers belong (left or right).

Step 4

1.   Now, close your eyes.
2.   Breathe in through the palm of your hand.
3.   Just allow that breathing energy in. Allow it go wherever it wants to go.

Step 5

1.   Continue the breathing.
2.   Feel the gentle pressure of the 2 fingers at your neck, gently pushing that breathing energy around your body.
3.   Now, allow that breathing energy to divide:
   -       part going down into your toes and out of your body
   -       part coming through your chest, into your head, and out of the top of your head
1.   Keep this going, gently.
4.   It begins to feel like you're floating on a cloud of that breathing energy.

PART 2

Step 1

1.   Now, feel a connection, in your head, with Second You: You$_2$.
2.   This is just you: yourself, looking at you.

3.   You₂ is floating, off the floor, an arm's length away.
4.   Allow You₂'s head to connect with yours.

Step 2
1.   From your 2 fingers at your neck, allow yourself to trace where in your back you feel the pain.
2.   Allow You₂ to see where the pain is.
3.   Allow You₂ to feel the pain.

Step 3
1.   Feel that connection, like a thread, between You₂'s head and that place of pain.
2.   Now, allow that pain to begin to move along that thread, to You₂.
3.   You can imagine the pain being carried in carriages of a train, along the thread, to You₂.

PART 3

Step 1
1.   Allow You₂ to send your relief.
2.   Feel You₂ sprinkling pain relief, like glitter, over your whole body.

Step 2
1.   Feel that You₂ glitter floating inside you, carried by that breathing energy, as it divides and floats inside you.
2.   Keep it going.

Step 3

1.   OK: relax
2.   Open your eyes.
3.   Breathe.

                              End.

Explaining

This is a multi-layered *Healing*. We do want to engage a link between your "computer" brain and your autonomic healing system. That's what the You2 Avatar connection does.

First we have to calm down the thoughts and feelings that are pressuring your head. What you're naturally doing, in response to that pressure, is to repress your Anxiety. You're drawing energy from doing that, and trying to use that energy to hold the pain at bay.

But that is toxic energy. It's actually making the pain worse. It's tiring you out trying keep the Anxiety repression going. This is reducing the ability of your body to heal. By trying to think ourselves better – by repressing Anxiety – we are actually making the pain worse.

So, with Part 1, we take your thinking head out of the problem. We are not letting your Anxiety rip. That would be too intense. Instead, we're gently allowing the Anxiety-Soothing Rhythm to work.

You're allowing some Anxiety in. That's what the 2 fingers attaching to your vagal nerve system are doing. And your focus on breathing, and allowing "energy" to divide and flow, is giving room for your Soothing to do its work.

That's why you start to feel floaty. The Soothing is getting your body-brain to release its natural tranquilizing pain-killers.

With this *Biomorphic* relief going on, we can start to connect your "computer" brain through *Psychotectics*, in Part 2. We're using the pain movement technique. That's going to be of limited effect, given the problem.

That's why we also bring the *You2 sprinkling pain relief*, in Part 3. The pain relief taps have been opened by the *Biomorphic* activity. Now, we're flooding the system with pain relief ordered up by your "computer" brain.

We're matching that pain relief, coming in, to the channels opened by the *Biomorphic* relief: *glitter floating inside you, carried by that breathing energy, as it divides and floats inside you.*

An anaesthetic works by blocking nerve signal transmission. That's what we're achieving here: just without the needle.

After Care

Until there's a physical resolution of the problem, the neuropathy will return. As it does, use the Recipe again.

You'll find that your mind and body respond to the *Healing* faster, and more deeply, as you repeat. After a few repetitions, you'll be able to get some of that relief, just by thinking of the Steps.

This is because you are engaging your "computer" brain to take over and link up with your autonomic functions. This is what works, rather than trying to "think your way" out of the pain, or to "block" the pain.

We do emphasise that this is only a sticking-plaster type of relief. You really must go see an appropriate clinical specialist. Your spine needs physical repair, and maintenance. We can help to change your experience of reality. But we can't change the physical reality, which is the landscape of your possible experiences.

21.   Hip Slip

Twists and slips to our hips are a common casualty of everyday life.

One client had suffered for years, following her healthy pregnancy and delivery. Sorting activities can contribute to this sort of problem. The wear and tear of age adds to the mix.

Scenario

The Client self-reports clicks, aches, soreness and general loss of well-being coming from the hip area.

Healing

Step 1

1.   You can sit down, or stand. Whatever works for you.
2.   Stretch your arms up.
3.   Hold.
4.   Breathe for 3 seconds.
5.   Let them drop.
6.   Relax.

Step 2

1.   Put the 2 fingers of each hand on your hips – the areas where you feel the ouch.
2.   Now, close your eyes.
3.   Feel a connection, in your head, with Second You: You$_2$.
4.   This is just you: yourself, looking at you.
5.   You$_2$ is directly behind you.
6.   Allow You$_2$'s head to connect with yours.

Step 3

1.   Allow You$_2$ to see where the pain is: as shown by your 2 fingers.
2.   Allow You$_2$ to feel the pain.
3.   Feel that connection, like a thread, between

You₂'s head and that place of pain.

Step 4

1. Allow your ghost self to move a moment out of your body.
2. It will slide out a little sideways.

Step 5

1. Take You₂'s wrists.
2. Move You₂'s fingers to the same place on You₂ as you feel the hip twist pain.
3. Now, keep holding onto You₂'s wrists and: *try to turn to look You₂ face on: directly in the eyes.*
4. Try to turn your shoulders to be parallel with You₂'s shoulders.
5. Try to move you ghost self, so that you're directly facing You₂.
6. Keep trying.
7. Keep trying.

Step 6

1. Relax.
2. Let the You₂ connection drop.
3. Come back into your Self.
4. Open your eyes.
5. Breathe.
6. Now, sit down for a few moments and breathe.

Step 7

1.   Now, stand.
2.   Feel your hips.
3.   Swivel your hips.
4.   Bend your knees.
5.   Lift your knees, one at a time.
6.   Swivel again.

End.

Explaining

Now, there's much less stiffness. No clicks. No, or low (subdued) pain.

Again, we're using *Morphonics*, within Congruence Interface Therapy (CIT), which is a branch of *Psychotectics*.

After Care

You'll get instant relief from the Steps.

But this is the type of injury that can return. As it does, just apply the Recipe. Using the Steps, even when you aren't being bothered by the pain, is also useful for helping your body not to fall into that state.

CHAPTER 7

ADDICTION ISSUES

We could spend an entire book focusing on addiction issues. In *Secret Self*, Chapter 7, we discuss the issues underlying addiction dynamics. It's stated in technical language below (if you don't want all the detail, feel free to skip to the next heading):

Much of our individual psychological problems come from interference in the ASR [Anxiety-Soothing Rhythm]. To function with psychological health, we need to able to allow the ASR to do its work. That's a perpetual dynamic, with us every moment of our lives from birth to death.

The ASR dynamic allows /S/<coherence>, at the perpetual price of decoherence:

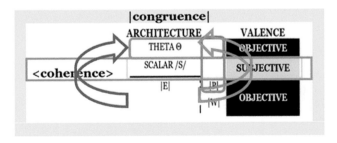

This dynamic is the core of what psychological science and spiritual learning seeks to describe as "Peace":

The Peace Bridge

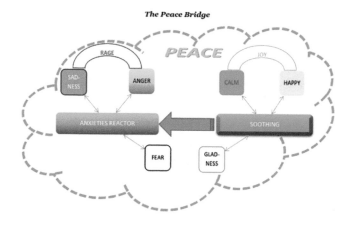

Peace is not a place. It is an emergent idealisation in {idents} of the movement which occurs from one moment of <coherence> to another: a series of bridges.

The ASR lives in disturbance. By |P| tunnelling through /S/ to stimulate <Constructs> which effect equalising I0|P| interaction.

Within the *Architecture* of Self, /S/ is an infinite but dimensioned continuum: a layer in the "sandwich". /S/ is limited by the architectural conditions of its own infinity.

By contrast, |P| is in infinite dynamic with the universe. The body replaces all of its atoms over the course of every 7 years.

We can and do create disturbances in our sea of {idents}. That's what <T>{i^n} and <F>{i^n} consist of. Yet we seek to contain novel {idents} in frameworks of <coherence>. For a fascinating example, see the phenomenon of visual prism adaptation.[9]

---

[9] Li A. Experiencing visuo-motor plasticity by prism adaptation in a classroom setting. *J Undergrad Neurosci Educ.* 2008;7(1):A13-A18.

When we experience difficulty in achieving <coherence>, then we resort to other devices. This is the route to psychological Pain.

Here, we need to differentiate between pain which us the result of physiological injury: a break, a burn. And what is often referred to as Emotional Pain.

The Pain Gap

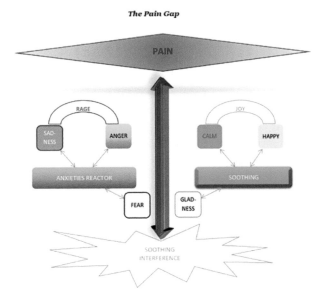

Pain is a place. Pain is failure of movement.

However, since both acts through signals in the |Exclusion Function|, the phenomenon of psychosomatic pain is as real to You, as externally attributable injury pain.

Indeed, it can be more enduring: many |P|hysiological injuries will heal, by themselves or with clinical treatment. But <coherence> induced pain is self-fulfilling.

It is an alignment of <coherence> to deal with life experience. In visual prism adaptation, special glasses invert left and right sight. Over some days, the wearer becomes used to the inversion. But then when the glasses are removed, a new <coherence> has to be established.

The wearer knows that it is "all in the mind". But that cannot stop the <coherence> function from orienting itself to sensory experience.

The fundamental dynamic of addiction issues lies in misaligned <coherence>. The problem is not the substance: it is the pain experienced by rigidified alignment of <coherence>, which repeats a dynamic of discomfort: "emotional pain".

The substance is of use only to blot out the pain: to effect temporary <decoherence> by having neurophysical effects. These are, of course, only temporary, and with various substances produce diminishing effects.

In all of this, what is being lost is the natural born dynamic of the ASR. <Anxiety> is not being allowed to regulate <Affect>. This prevents the <soothing> dynamic from engaging reactively. The result is a "frozen" place of Pain.

We see here another of the paradoxes of Self:
- Our /S/ubjective <self> layer needs to create and multiply {idents} in order to allow our Personality lattice to become whole: to become a <Me>.
- We perpetually seek <coherence> so as to shape that explosion of {idents}, so as to create the core {idents} of <Me>. In other words, to establish homeostasis of <self> recognition.
- Yet, it is that very dynamic that tends towards dislocation and suppression of the ASR. We can see that most clearly in the journey from infant to maturity.

We judge maturity by capacity for self-control. Yet that type of control is secured through ASR suppression, using powerful cultural Mimetics.

This is not to suggest that the healthy state of <coherence> is at war with the ASR: that being an emotionally incontinent individual is a truer "self".

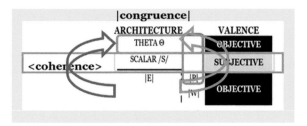

On the contrary, the attribution of /S/{ident} <coherence> to ASR activity, is exactly what best provides control: because that control arises dynamically from the process itself: without necessity for <coherence> of <T>{i^n} or <F>{i^n}.

It's how baby You learns. It's actually how the mature Self learns also. It's the most powerful heuristic available to the Self.

The science of Biomorphics concerns the location of pathways that energetically activate the ASR, without "challenging" <coherence>.

This recalibrates |congruence|. That re-assertion of the *Architecture* within which the /S/ continuum enjoys {identation} infinity, automatically alters the self-reflection of <cohered> {idents}.

The Addiction Dynamic

Addictions come in lots of different types: substance issues; activity issues. We can get to the central force of the addiction dynamic, by asking a simple question: *why do we do it?*

We all know that the answer is: *to make us feel better*. The problem with addiction is, that this is a perfectly sensible answer. According to some eminent philosophers who've been saying it for 2,500 years (the modern ones – since the 19th century - being called Utilitarians), that's pretty much why anyone does anything: the pleasure-seeking principle.

It's not mad – or bad – to seek to anaesthetise pain, or to seek pleasure. We all do it. But there are mad – and bad – ways of doing it. If someone were addicted to breathing, or looking at blue sky, in order to get a feeling of feeling better, we'd find it odd to suggest that they have an addiction problem. Some people find it difficult to go an hour without a cup of tea. But we don't feel the need to want to send them to rehab.

Tea, we might say, is not a mind-altering substance. Well, it is. Everything we ingest alters our minds. Now, we're not here trying to wash – or wish – away, the awful personal and social consequences of addiction-centred lifestyles. What we need to do, is recognise that "addicts" are not a breed apart. They are going through the same dynamics that everyone alive does. But they are choosing to try and solve their problems in ways that only a small percentage of people do.

We know that some people can "handle it". They can use powerful drugs socially, for fun. Then forget about it and go about their ordinary lives. Then there are those who can't. What's the difference between one group and another? The *addiction dynamic*.

Let's get some clarity around what is not at the root of the addiction dynamic. It's not memory. As we saw in Part 3, memories are ideas we make up, every day. We make them up differently each time we remember. That's why we can "wipe" traumatic memories so easily, with *Matrixial Healing* Techniques.

We don't carry traumatic wounds from our childhood. We might want to think that we do. But that doesn't make it so. When we say "I can still see... [that awful memory]": well, we can't. What we can see is a picture that we decide to imagine, right now. We control that visualisation. We can make it big or small, darker or lighter. We control the way we look at it. We use that control, so as to pretend to ourselves that the memory controls us.

We are interfering with our *Anxiety-Soothing Rhythm*, to make the imagined picture seem more emotionally real. We do that moment by moment. We try to justify the repressing of our Anxiety, by referring to memory ideas, which we also make up moment by moment. We are justifying self-harming behaviour by reference to an imaginary voice from the past.

The serial killer might justify harming others, by reference to an imaginary voice from the present. The difference is that, the true psychopath can't tell the difference between imagination and reality. We can.

We get into a frozen place of Pain by interfering with our ASR. To try and self-heal, we keep interfering - by trying to anaesthetise the unnecessary Pain. The depressive dynamic tries to stay inside its own circle: to reduce the apparent effect of the Pain, by disconnecting from the world of experience. The addiction dynamic looks outside its own circle: to limit the Pain by seeking outside distraction (chemical, activity). The effect of that distraction is to disconnect from the world of experience: you jack in, to tune out.

In this Chapter, we look at core *Matrixial Healing* Techniques that can help to change these dynamics. How long it takes for the Healing to work, after the instant hit you get from the Recipe, depends on how long and how deep we have let the dynamic run.

By repeated use of the Recipes, we do create patterns in our "computer" brain. These counteract the thinking/ feeling brain dynamics. That happens automatically. We find that the hole we're trying to hide in gets smaller.

There are rehab techniques and centres, help groups and other therapies. Anyone concerned by their condition should try those out too. *Matrixial Healing* Techniques are not intended to be a substitute. They can make those life-saving approaches more successful.

22. Depression

You may wonder what a section on Depression is doing in a Chapter about Addiction Issues. The answer is that Depression is the primary addiction of hundreds of millions of people. What we often think of as "addiction" is really *depression-plus*: depression with substance abuse; depression sought to be neutralised by activities that harm oneself or others.

Depression manifests with symptoms everyone recognises:

- lack of energy
- physical ailments
- isolation.

We can broadly recognise this as a loss of connected-ness. The sufferer loses connection with themselves. Loses connection with the outside world: partners, friends, family. Loses connection with the positive aspects of activities in the world.

We could look at the state of depression and suggest that the individual is suffering from "over-soothing". That they are self-soothing so much, as to be unable to get off the sofa, or out of bed.

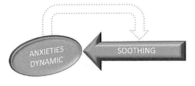

But we know, from *Matrixial Science,* that this can't be correct. The *Anxiety-Soothing Rhythm* doesn't work like that. Soothing responds, under stimulus, in a way which always matches the Anxiety.

This shows us the real problem is not too much Soothing: it's a dysfunction in Anxiety.

The depressive mindset builds a fear around Anxiety. A fear that, if Anxiety were allowed to get "out of control", then it would overwhelm the sufferer. So, what we first need to do is conquer that fear.

We don't get there by talking about it. A person suffering from depression is repressing their Anxiety. One way to do this, is to create Shadow Slices Ш.

Our thinking/feeling brain is illuminated by mirrors. Reflection is the essential process for doing our thinking in /S/. We reflect one association of ideas off another, and so measure their difference or similarity: good evil; right/ wrong; truth/lies.

We create models of these idea associations and then use those as reference points. We attach "emotions" to these associations to make them more powerful. These become our "emotional layers": what we think of as the fundamental elements of our emotional personality.

It's neither easy nor automatic for the 5 Slices to relate in dynamic harmony. All the circumstances of life conspire to de-harmonise, to interfere with the natural "gravity" of our personality.

We can find that the mirroring function doesn't work, or just doesn't seem to work. That perception is probably justified. There's no law of science or nature that says that we must be able to understand our life experiences.

We create understandings: and those are more or less efficient to the circumstances of our life. To maintain <coherence> what we all do is create Shadow Slices (Ш): a *Shadow Slice Ш is an association of ideas that is unaffected by the dynamics of the Slices.*

The result is that our <Feelings> and <Thoughts> churn. We feel upset and unbalanced. The Ш sits in our "attic" headspace, as if surrounded by emotional fires and sirens. Whatever we think and feel, we can't shift the Ш obsession. We are *obsessed*. And possessed by the powerlessness we feel.

The process of attaching "emotions" to thoughts is going on perpetually, every moment of the day. But this is not so with Ш. These Ш appear out of our ordinary efforts to get <coherence> in our thinking and feeling, relation to the unfamiliar: to work out what's going on in our life, and why. We manufacture Ш without positively intending to.

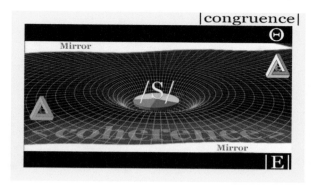

The "impossible triangles" represent Ш Shadow Slices.

What we then discover is that we can power Ш by undertaking active repression of our Anxiety:

- Our <Anxiety> is going about its usual business.
- But, within /S/ (our thinking/feeling brain), we are deliberately suppressing normal attachment of "emotions" to thoughts.
- So, we are reducing the gravitational force, or size, of the Slices.
- The Mirrors become "starved" of reflective {ident} input, and so output less reflection.
- We thus alter <coherence>.
- <Anxiety> is not reaching Θ<Constructs>.
- Our Ш gains more relative size.

So, our Objective Behavior is being altered:

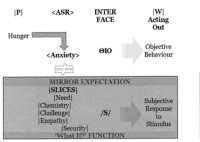

This affects our ability to undertake the "what if" function

It also affects our "how, why?" function

It is commonplace to notice these aspects of Ш, of obsession:

- We become "unidimensional".
- Our ordinary Personality appears to others to become more narrowly focused.
- Emotion and Thought appear disconnected.
- We can appear highly emotional, or emotionally repressed, but the obsession endures.

We can't talk our way out of, or be talked out of, this awful cycle of Anxiety repression.

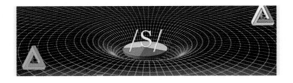

We just turn more ideas, and feelings associated with ideas, into more of these "impossible triangles" Ш. In fact, talking can make matters *worse*. It makes these "impossible triangle" type ideas seem more real.

So, when people suffering depression say "I don't want to talk about it", that comes from a healthy instinct of mental and emotional self-preservation. If your eyes are closed because you're standing on the edge of a skyscraper, then "opening up" is not wise.

So, the depressive problem is, ultimately, a problem with Anxiety. What the sufferer needs, is to be able to experience Anxiety, and so to experience the matching Soothing.

Scenario
The Client self-reports depression. The Client may be taking GP prescribed medication. This will be making the Shadow Slice Ш and Anxiety repression problems worse. We would recommend consultation with the GP to find a pathway off medication.

We divide the Healing into three parts:
(1)   getting the Client to visualise the walls which they are creating between themselves and their experiences;
(2)   stimulating Anxiety safely;
(3)   feeling the natural boundaries made available by normal functioning of the ASR.

Then, we want to achieve balance. To allow the Client to feel the power of just being themselves.

Healing

PART 1 WALLS

Step 1

1.   Sit down for this one.
2.   Go inside your head.
3.   Find the Walls that you like to feel around you, protecting you.

Step 2

1.   You can open or close your eyes as you wish for this next part.
2.   Stretch your arms, with open palms: to your left or right side.
3.   Feel that Wall.
4.   Feel with your arms and palms like you're pushing at that Wall.
5.   Push, really push.
6.   Feel that your Wall is solid.

Step 3

1.   Feel that solid Wall.
2.   Feel how you feel about that: about the Wall being there.
3.   Feel how it makes you feel.
4.   Imagine 3 holes appearing in the Wall.
5.   Feel how you feel about those holes.

Step 4

1.   Feel how you can fill the holes up: making the Wall solid again.
2.   Fill the holes up.
3.   Feel your Wall: solid and protecting.

Step 5

1.   OK, you know where to find the Wall, any time.
2.   Let's keep it there for later.
3.   For now: relax.
4.   Breathe.

End.

PART 2 ANXIETY

Step 1

1.   Find some alone space.
2.   Sit down anywhere comfortable.
3.   Take the top two fingers of whatever is your writing hand.
4.   Place those fingers gently on the waist side of your tummy. (You can find the location simply by placing your two fingers over your belly button, then moving them around to your writing hand side).
5.   Rest your fingers at that spot.
6.   Close your eyes.
7.   Breathe normally.

Step 2

1.   Take the top two fingers of your other hand.
2.   Place them gently at the back of your neck, on
        the other side of your body from your other
        fingers. (Location is anywhere between the nape
        of your neck and your collar-bone: just gently
        move your fingers till you find a spot that feels
        fine to you).
3.   Breathe normally.

Step 3: Take 1 to 2 Minutes

1.   Feel a connection between your fingers.
2.   A connection running through your upper body.
        Like a wire.
3.   You may feel it hot. You may feel it cold.
4.   If it's a hot connection, allow it to get hotter. If
        it's a cold connection, allow it to get colder.
5.   Allow the connection to become more intense.
6.   Feel it like the filament in a light bulb, getting
        brighter as you turn up the voltage.
7.   Allow yourself to allow those toxic energy
        feelings to run through that connection.
8.   Between your fingers, it feels like angry electric
        ants scurrying around.
9.   It feels like the connection is becoming barbed
        wire, spilling toxic chemicals into your body.
10.   Let the angry energy become more intense.
11.   And more. Filling your chest and your head.

Step 4

1. Now it's coursing through you. That toxic writhing energy.
2. Take the hand with the fingers which are at your waist.
3. Take the palm of that hand.
4. Place it gently over the centre of your chest.
5. Still feel the angry toxic energy coursing through you.

Step 5

1. Now, you're going in a few moments to take a huge breath in.
2. Through your nose or your mouth.
3. However you'd do it if you were about to jump into a swimming pool.
4. Big breath in: *Now.*
5. Hold that breath for 3 long seconds.
6. One … Two … Three…
7. Let it out, and at the same time, press your palm into your chest.
8. You can fall back into your chair, or into a lying position, if you like.
9. Rest. Breathe normally.
10. Think whatever thoughts you think. Feel whatever feelings you feel.

End.

PART 3 POWER

Step 1

1.   Close your eyes.
2.   Go back to where you were stretching your arms, with open palms.
3.   Now, push at that Wall. Push. Push it away.
4.   Ok: you can't feel anything there.

Step 2

1.   See if you can imagine holes appearing in the wall.
2.   Push with your hands. See if you can feel any holes.
3.   Ok: you can't feel anything there.

End.

PART 4 BALANCE

Step 1

1.   Find some alone space.
2.   Sit down anywhere comfortable.
3.   Allow yourself to feel as jittery as you often do.

Step 2

1.   Take the palm of your writing hand.
2.   Place it over your tummy: just where your tummy button is.
3.   Make sure to leave a little gap between your palm and your tummy. This is really important.

The gap should be a finger-width.

4.   Close your eyes now.
5.   Focus on breathing in through the palm of your hand.
6.   Feel yourself drawing in breaths, through the palm of your hand.
7.   Remember how when you were inside your mummy, that's where your life support came into your body.
8.   You can breathe deep or shallow. Slow or fast. Whatever works.

Step 3

1.   Your eyes are still closed.
2.   Take the palm of your other hand.
3.   Place it over your chest.
4.   Make sure to leave a little gap between your palm and your chest. This is really important. The gap should be a finger-width.
5.   Focus on breathing out through the palm of your hand.
6.   Feel yourself pushing out breaths, through the palm of your hand.
7.   Just do this for as long as you feel you like it.

End.

Explaining

This is experienced for the first time, usually as a sudden

beam of sunlight. Just the fact that – for a few moments – the pain of depression stops, is enough to have a big change on how the Client views their situation.

The Wall Technique gets the Client to replace an artificial, imaginary "Wall", with the natural boundary that exists between every individual and the world. That boundary is felt in the balance that comes from your Self. That you feel inside as You. As you gain that feeling, the artificial Wall just fades away.

The holes we get the Client to visualise, are kind of the excuses that the Client makes to themselves. It's the Anxiety-repressed way, of creating a fake "anxiety" which you can fix. You create little worries that you can then put to bed. But it's not all plain sailing. Because you're having to invest massive amounts of energy to keep that Wall up. You can lose control of the little worry holes. They can turn into fractures, which you can't control. That stimulates your fear. So, now you're limping round, trying to fix non-existent holes in a non-existent wall.

But it seems utterly real to you. More real than anything "out there" in the world. Because you're disconnected from your own world of experience.

We get you to challenge that fake Wall, with real Anxiety: and the Anxiety-Soothing Rhythm wins. It always does. With the *Angel Wings* Technique, we restore balance. From which you automatically draw peace and power.

After Care

When we're dealing with a long-term depressive state, this isn't going to be an instant fix. We are trying to heal a habit - a long ingrained practice – of Anxiety repression.

Now, you feel connections that you hadn't felt for a while. The ASR framework that's running in you again, allows you to cope with those experiences. What we're looking to achieve is for you to feel challenged by experiences, and to respond by allowing Anxiety to give you motivation, and Soothing to balance that out.

We're replacing a motivation to suppress Anxiety, with a motivation to enjoy the balance, peace and power which comes from letting the ASR run.

This *Healing* takes time, for repetition. The Client takes whichever Parts work best for them, and repeat as often as they feel it's helpful. After a while, the "computer" brain lays down patterns. You just have to think of an idea which used to imprison you in depression, and your ASR kick-starts automatically. Now, you're healing yourself.

23.   Substances

Substance addiction comes in many shapes and sizes. Laws around the world draw different political, and policing policy-driven, distinctions, between different substances. Fatty foods contribute to many more deaths worldwide than crack. But, because one is encouraged, and the other is criminalised, serious economic dislocations are introduced. Nobody has to join a criminal gang to supply Oreos.

Yet, the underlying dynamic is the same. It works on two levels:

(1)   chemical craving;

(2)   psychological craving.

When chemical craving is strong enough, we will make any psychological adjustments necessary to go along with it. Until we stop. Let's try and disconnect the chemical from the psychological.

Scenario

The Client self-reports substance addiction issues. The type of substance is irrelevant to the addiction dynamic.

23A   Chemical Healing

Step 1

1.   You can sit down, or stand. Whatever works for you.

2.   Look inside you. Feel the place where the craving feels worst.

3.   Take the top 2 fingers of your writing hand.

4.   Place them gently on your body, at that worst place.

Step 2

1.   Now, close your eyes.

2.   Feel a connection, in your head, with Second You: You₂.

3.   This is just you: yourself, looking at you.

4.   You₂ is just by your shoulder.

5.   Allow You₂'s head to connect with yours.

Step 3

1.   Allow You₂ to see where the pain place is: as shown by your 2 fingers.

2.   Allow You₂ to feel the pain.

Step 4

1.   Feel that connection, like a thread, between You₂'s head and that place of pain.

2.   You may feel some resistance. That's normal.

Step 5

1.   Ordinary You needs to take a step back.

2.   Think of ordinary You as being able to take a tiny step back outside yourself: like a ghost or a spirit.

3.   Just let that ghost or spirit take a tiny step back out of yourself.

Step 6

1.   Let that ghost or spirit you use whatever sub stance it likes to use.

2.   Just allow the ghost or spirit you to feel whatever it feels.

Step 7

1.   Feel that connection, like a thread, between You2's head and that place of pain.
2.   Allow that pain to begin to move along that thread, to You2.
3.   Keep it going.

Step 8

1.   Connect with You2's head and body.
2.   Stroke You2: get You2 to release the healing which makes the pain go away.
3.   There's resistance there.
4.   Just push softly through the resistance.
5.   There: now the pain in You2 is going away, with the healing.

Step 9

1.   The You2 connection can drop.
2.   Ghost or spirit you, can come back into yourself.

Step 10

1.   OK: relax
2.   Open your eyes.
3.   Breathe.

End.

Explaining

The critical element is at Step 6. Instead of just saying "no" to drugs, we allow that version of "you" to go for it. Knock yourself out with the substance (imaginatively).

The Avatar connection (You2) is engaging your "computer" brain. Getting your natural healing process going.

This automatically produces an "aha!" moment inside us. There's this realisation of a process which offers healing, and which has nothing to do with the substance. We're creating *distance* between:

(1)   chemical craving;
(2)   psychological craving.

Under the addiction dynamic, there is no such distance. Talk, talk, talking about things, however rational, spiritual or empathic, doesn't change the distance. You have to *experience* it.

Now you have. The user you was off in the corner, doing what it does, with whatever substance. Fully engaged and indulged. Yet the pain was getting (even a little bit) healed *by something else*.

After Care
Obviously, the Client can be encouraged to use this *Healing*, as often as they like. We want "computer" brain patterns to become formed. So that, each time our thinking / feeling mind reaches for the addiction dynamic, that *Healing* pattern gets triggered.

Warning label: success with this *Healing* is going to lead to frustration. The Client has come to feel reliant on the addiction dynamic. This creation and reinforcement of distance is disorienting and irritating. So, we need other *Healing,* to work towards undermining and replacing the dynamic.

23B   *Anticipation Healing*
PART 1

Step 1

1.   Close your eyes.
2.   See yourself getting into your car.
3.   It can be the car you have.
4.   Or a dream car: G Wagon, Rolls-Royce: whatever.
5.   Sit comfortably behind the wheel. Adjust your seat.
6.   It may be day or night: that's up to you.

Step 2

1.   Look in your rear-view mirror.
2.   See yourself using: whatever it is you like to use.
3.   Just watch in the rear-view mirror.
4.   Open your eyes.
5.   Blink a few times.

PART 2

Step 1

1.   Close your eyes.

2. Be back in your car again.
3. Look through the windscreen and see that's it's dark
4. Now, find your feelings that allow you to turn the headlights on.

Step 2

1. Turn those headlights on.
2. Turn them as bright as you like.

Step 3

1. Now, try to see yourself using.
2. Try to see that in the headlights.
3. Open your eyes.
4. Blink a few times.

PART 3

Step 1

1. Close your eyes.
2. Be back in your car again.
3. You're in the passenger seat,

Step 2

1. Try to see yourself using, in the driver's seat.
2. The driver's seat has control of the rear-view mirror.
3. The driver's seat has control of the headlights.
4. Try to see yourself, in the driver's seat: using.

Step 3

1.   OK: relax
2.   Open your eyes.
3.   Breathe.

End.

Explaining

The previous *Healing* was about creating distance. This is about *rejection*.

You can see yourself in the rear-view mirror, because that's your thinking mind: always looking at the past. That's how all thinking works: as a reflection up the past. When we try to see that same idea in the "headlights" future of our feelings: we can't see it.

We just think that we have feelings about the substance. We don't. We may well have chemical processes. But those go in every moment of time inside us. Every breath, heartbeat and brain activity is a chemical process. But those are not "feelings". It's the thoughts we wrap around the senses of these processes which makes them "feelings".

So, we can't see those thoughts (always about the past), in the future of our feelings.

In Part 3, we put all this together. The Client is holding on to control of their thoughts (seen in the rear-view mirror) and feelings (seen in the headlights). Yet now, what appears as a stranger, is trying to use them, while using. The scene just doesn't make sense. The Client rejects the image proposed.

In doing that, the Client is rejecting themselves as a user. That's a big thing. A powerful insight: that the Client can really see their self clearly. Under the addiction dynamic, this is a viewpoint that seems to have become lost. Now, it's not only seen, but experienced.

After Care

This Healing is more of a one-off. As the "computer" brain creates the patterns from other *Healing*, it becomes harder to see oneself in the rear-view mirror at all.

23C   *Craving Healing*
PART 1

Step 1

1.   Sit down for this one.
2.   Go inside your head.
3.   Find those feelings of Craving.

Step 2

1.   Hold your arms out in front of you.
2.   Cup your hands.
3.   Now, take those Craving feelings.
4.   Allow the weight of that Craving to become a

      super-heavy ball.

5.   Drop that super-heavy Craving ball in your hands.

6.   Allow your hands to fall, as the weight forces your hands down.

7.   Allow your arms to sag.

8.   Feel the weight of that Cravings ball, in your hands: in your lap.

9.   Close your hands over it. Hold it. Protect it, like an injured bird.

Step 3

1.   OK, you know where to find the Craving feelings, any time.

2.   Let's keep it there for later.

3.   For now: relax.

4.   Breathe.

PART 2

Step 1

1.   Take the top two fingers of whatever is your writing hand.

2.   Place those fingers gently on the waist side of your tummy. (You can find the location simply by placing your two fingers over your belly button, then moving them around to your writing hand side).

3.   Rest your fingers at that spot.

4.   Close your eyes.

5.   Breathe normally.

Step 2

1.   Take the top two fingers of your other hand.
2.   Place them gently at the back of your neck, on the other side of your body from your other fingers. (Location is anywhere between the nape of your neck and your collar-bone: just gently move your fingers till you find a spot that feels fine to you).
3.   Breathe normally.

Step 3: Take 1 to 2 Minutes

1.   Feel a connection between your fingers.
2.   A connection running through your upper body. Like a wire.
3.   You may feel it hot. You may feel it cold.
4.   If it's a hot connection, allow it to get hotter. If it's a cold connection, allow it to get colder.
5.   Allow the connection to become more intense.
6.   Feel it like the filament in a light bulb, getting brighter as you turn up the voltage.
7.   Allow yourself to allow those toxic energy feelings to run through that connection.
8.   Between your fingers, it feels like angry electric ants scurrying around.
9.   It feels like the connection is becoming barbed wire, spilling toxic chemicals into your body.
10.   Let the angry energy become more intense.

11.   And more. Filling your chest and your head.

Step 4

1.   Now it's coursing through you. That toxic writhing energy.
2.   Take the hand with the fingers which are at your waist.
3.   Take the palm of that hand.
4.   Place it gently over the centre of your chest.
5.   Still feel the angry toxic energy coursing through you.

Step 5

1.   Now, you're going in a few moments to take a huge breath in.
2.   Through your nose or your mouth.
3.   However you'd do it if you were about to jump into a swimming pool.
4.   Big breath in: *Now*.
5.   Hold that breath for 3 long seconds.
6.   One ... Two ... Three...
7.   Let it out, and at the same time, press your palm into your chest.
8.   You can fall back into your chair, or into a lying position, if you like.
9.   Rest. Breathe normally.
10.   Think whatever thoughts you think. Feel what ever feelings you feel.

PART 3

Step 1

1. Go back to where you were holding that Cravings ball in your hands.
2. Cup your hands.
3. Feel for that ball.
4. That super-heavy Cravings ball.
5. Ok: you can't feel anything there.

Step 2

1. Open your eyes.
2. Relax.
3. Maybe stand up and shake out.

End.

Explaining

We've done *Healings* to experience distance and rejection. Now, we're enabling the experience of: nothing.

We're using the familiar Technique of burning through an obsession (in this case, a psychological craving), with real Anxiety. Allowing the ASR to work, so that the Soothing is intense – to match intense Anxiety. That Soothing comes naturally from within. Not an anaesthetic from outside.

After Care

This is a *Healing* that we'd like the Client to repeat. Again, we want to create those "computer" brain patterns. We also want to open up access to the ASR. To stop Anxiety repression. To allow the Client to feel the intense Soothing which can come from it.

Instead of a numb, anaesthetic, nothingness: the Client experiences balance, peace and power. The Steps are short. The road to travel can be long. But the final destination is clear and possible: it's coming back to You.

24.   Activities

The addiction dynamic is just the same, whether the focus is a substance or an activity. Or even a food or beverage. We are still looking for something outside ourselves, not to change us, but to stay the same. To stay true to whatever "distorted" view of ourselves we are choosing to have.

So, we can use the same *Healing* Techniques as in the previous Section. We can also use an Avatar Dialogue Therapy Technique.

Scenario

The Client self-reports activity addiction issues. The type of activity is irrelevant to the addiction dynamic.

Healing

Step 1

1.   Close your eyes.
2.   Breathe.

3.   Be at home, in living room or bedroom.
4.   There's a mirror in the room.

Step 2

1.   There's a knock at the door.
2.   Open, and invite Other You to come in.

Step 3

1.   Look at Other You.
2.   See whatever it is that you don't like about Other You.
3.   You can see the appearance of Other You: see what you don't like about it.
4.   You can see inside the head of Other You: see what you don't like about it.
5.   You can see the Personality of Other You: see what you don't like about it.

Step 4

1.   Breathe.
2.   Take Other You over to the mirror.
3.   Now, try to see Other You, in the mirror.
4.   Try.

Step 5

1.   Now, look around the room for Other You.
2.   OK: they've gone.

Step 6

1.   Open your eyes.
2.   Relax.

End.

Explaining

We tend to think that we see ourselves, that we can see ourselves, in our worst light. We want to believe that we have "internalised" that view: made it part of us – of who we are. Thinking like that gives us a great excuse for being unable to change it.

Yet, it's all an illusion. We don't really have that view. It's a fantasy which we create, and then have to keep feeding energy to, in order to keep it going.

This is what the mirror shows us. It's often surprising when we can't actually see that view in the mirror. That's why we have to try. Yet the harder we try, the less what we think we want to see comes into focus.

Well, you might ask, how does that stop me doing the harmful activities I was doing? It doesn't. But it does change how you experience those activities. You can't load them onto this fantasy you anymore.[10] It's you doing this to yourself. That hurts. We tend not to like doing things to ourselves that really hurt.

---

[10] For a great insight, read *The Picture of Dorian Gray*. Oscar Wilde (1890)

After Care

This is a one-off *Healing*. We can repeat, but with smaller effects.

25.   Family Members

The Author has spent much time working with family members and addiction issues. The best core advice is the 3 Cs:[11]

The three Cs of addiction recovery will help you better understand how you can support someone working toward their recovery.

It is never easy to watch someone you love struggle with an illness, but the three Cs of addiction recovery can help you support your loved one in their addiction recovery journey while also maintaining your own personal boundaries, says Katia S. Stoletniy, MD, addiction psychiatrist at Loma Linda University Behavioral Medicine Center.

"I didn't cause it."

One of the most important things to remember about addiction is that you did not cause your loved one's addictive behaviors.

"Although your loved one may cast blame at you, you must understand you did not cause it," Stoletniy says. "Understanding what is and isn't under your control is the first step to set healthy boundaries and help your loved one in their journey to recovery."

"I can't cure it."

Addiction is a chronic disease, like diabetes or hypertension, and requires guidance from a medical professional. Addressing addiction requires both physical and mental lifestyle changes, Stoletniy says. Treatment options may include medical management of withdrawal symptoms, cognitive behavioral therapy, or residential rehabilitation. It can also include a combination of different treatments.

"I can't control it."

Addiction is a biological disease that affects the brain's chemistry. You might feel the urge to try to take control of your loved one's actions, but letting go of that urge will enable you to

---

[11] https://www.webmd.com/connect-to-care/addiction-treatment-recovery/reference/three-cs-addiction-recovery

THE MATRIXIAL HEALING HANDBOOK: Instant Therapy Recipes

engage more productively and focus your energy on what you
can change.
You can educate yourself about addiction and take care of
yourself as you support your loved one on their path to recovery.
"When your loved one is ready to ask for help, you will be there
to support them and make the right call," Stoletniy says.

The *Healing* we are trying to provide, in this context, is all
about getting distance: supported detachment. When we
go to a doctor for help with a day-to-day physical illness,
we don't expect the doctor to become emotionally involved.

What we want, is professional detachment. The emotional
distance that allows the doctor to assess our problem and
prescribe medical solutions: realistically. A matter of
science, not soul.

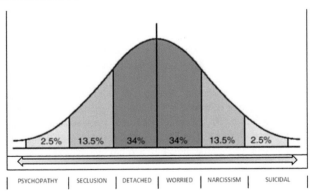

In dealing with a person suffering serious addiction
problems, we need to be aware that the addict will
be able to display three pathologies of personality,

simultaneously:

(1)   Psychopathy.

(2)   Narcissistic Personality Disorder.

(3)   Suicidal Ideation.

Psychopathy

As we explained in Chapter 7 of *I Want To Love But*:[12]

> Because of this, we can have sympathy for their condition: which is not their fault. But we are entitled to protection from their anti-social acting out. How we achieve that protection (fryin' 'em; prison; psych ward; care in the community; letting them run for elected office) is a debate outside this book.
>
> The one thing we can't feel for a Psychopath is Empathy: because that is their Missing Slice. That's why we are so fascinated by them.
>
> To add accuracy, the Psychopath:
> - Has a completely missing Empathy Slice; or
> - One that's small in proportion to the other 4 Slices; or
> - Doesn't relate well to the other 4 Slices.
>
> As we saw in Chapter 5:
> Empathy is a meeting place, between people, without Wants or Satisfaction. Empathy neither

---

seeks nor needs any reward.

Empathy is simply the recognition in others of what we can see in our own *My-Space*. The more that another's *My-Space* resembles our own, the easier the Empathy. The more intense the Empathy.

Lacking Empathy, the Psychopath simply cannot see Others as People. The Psychopath doesn't see him/her Self as part of a population of people, like him/her Self. That's why the Bell Curve does not exist for a Psychopath.

The Psychopath stands apart, truly special and unique: the ruler of his/her own world. Which is just how a toddler sees the world. The Psychopath is stuck in infancy: at pre-7YO.

…

Experience:

Imagine Ted Bundy running past his yellow VW, chasing a college girl across a cold Colorado car park, at night. His legs are pumping, his breath is panting in frosty air. He grips a tyre iron tightly in one fist.

Now imagine you can freeze that frame, and:
- tap Bundy (safely) on the shoulder.
- Just ask Bundy: "What are you feeling?"

You know what happens. He turns slowly to stare you straight in the face. Bundy says: "Huh? Nothin."

Bundy is not involved with Emotions. If he has any at all, he has no connection with them. The Concrete floor is rock solid. That's partly why he keeps behaving anti-socially: to keep it that way. Another reason is: because he can.

Bundy will calmly explain to you: "That thing isn't doing what I want."

"What thing?" we ask.

"Uh, that thing running away?" Bundy replies.

"You mean the screaming terrified girl?"

"Whatever…" grunts Bundy.

You see, to Bundy, she is just an object.

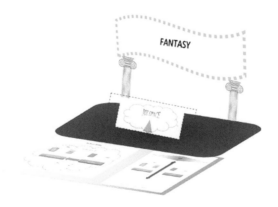

…Instead, Bundy has PsychoLand. A Disneyworld for the insane. It can be a rich and colourful place. Or just dull. Or boring. It depends how smart Psycho is. There are plenty of smart, and plenty of dumb Psychopaths.

Most are of average IQ: as you would expect.

PsychoLand operates under whatever logic works for Psycho. It can be that dead things are good, so it's good to make things dead. It can be that a twig is god and should be worshipped and preserved.

The only rules are the rules Psycho decrees for PsychoLand, and they can be changed with a wave of the royal Psycho hand. After all, it's not like Psycho needs to ask anyone else's permission.

Psychos are their own fan club of one. That's both very powerful: and very fragile.

So, in Bundy's PsychoLand, the thing running away is like a badly behaving toy for a 3 year old: Smash. Smash. Thump.

"Timmy: why are you hitting Buzz Lightyear on the ground like that?", we ask.
Smash. Smash. Thump.

"'Cos he's not fwyin' pwopewy Dada."

To choose a word that fits Timmy's mental state (he has not formed and emotional personality yet, and has no knowledge of love), Timmy is *Frustrated*. There is Frustration at the object that is not complying with Timmy's ToyLand rules.

Timmy will grow up. Psycho never does.

Psycho wants things. Psycho wants these strange "people" objects to do things. Psycho wants them to provide food at the café, and sell clothes at the clothes shop, and make Psycho's life convenient. Like standing still while Psycho hits them.

Psycho has learned to watch what human-things do, and copy them. Psycho doesn't get why bags of skin say "Good Morning" to each other. But they do, and it seems to get a nice response, so just do it. So, Psycho *copies* the behaviours of average bags of skin. Psycho is a copycat. The smarter Psycho is, the better the copying.

As we conclude:

You can't *reason* with Psycho. For You and I, however wacky our thoughts and feelings get, they live in our Emotional *Me Space*. They are real, because our *Anxiety-Soothing* dance, is real. It shapes our lives with every heartbeat.

But you can't use *emotional intelligence* in PsychoLand. The only rules are the rules Psycho invents. They are self-contradictory, upside down, totally crazy to us. But to Psycho, they are the only logic Psycho knows.

We can't Control and we can't Cure psychopathically-based acting out.

Narcissistic Personality Disorder
We are born to operate out thoughts and feelings (the grey and purple arrows)

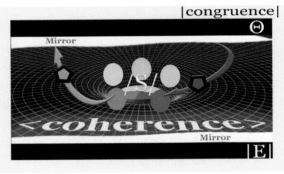

by reflecting them from internal mirrors. This is the Architecture of our brain. When we don't work out thoughts and feelings like this, then we create those awkward Shadow Slices Ш.

So, Narcissism is "baked in" to the very structure of how we come to be personalities. To say that Narcissism is somehow wrong, is like suggesting that having 2 arms and 2 legs is wrong.

Narcissistic Personality Disorder ("NPD") is a completely different matter. It's a dynamic that is harmful to others and self-harming. The core of NPD is that the sufferer feels that they cannot control their thoughts and feelings. So they try to control everything and everyone around them, instead.

We could put it this way: the NPD sufferer is trying to use you as their mirror, because they don't trust their own internal mirrors to work properly. Imagine how frightening it must be to allow another person to have that degree of control over your thoughts and feelings: ever been head over heels in love?

Of course, the difference between two people sharing love, and an NPD sufferer and victim, is that the NPD sufferer is not sharing anything. Which makes their isolation even more terrifying.

You place your wall mirror on the wall and at the height that you want: right? It's important. The positioning needs to be just so. You need to be able to rely on that reflection. So, the NPD sufferer needs to control you and your position: because you are their mirror. That's how it works from their perspective. Which is both entirely rational and completely mad.

As we explained in Chapter 7 of *I Want To Love But*:[13]

> Narc can see the whole Engine chugging away. Every cog, wheel, valve, wire. Every connection. That's why the Narc can pull Your strings so well. But there's the Pain gap. The Engine does not work

---

[13] The Author (2019)

so as to generate a Personality in *Me Space*. The Narc can see all the connections so clearly, because they are frozen in pain.

Seeing is not Being
But Being, requires Seeing

The Narc demonstrates this so well. The Narc can See: but the Pain stops Narc Being. Of course, it's the Narc actually putting that Pain in there, every moment.

The disconnection between Me Space and the Engine leaves a void: a vacuum. This is the Narc void, into which floods Narc fantasies.

Meet a Narcissist

This is a really complex framework, compared

to the Psycho. And (unlike Psychos) there are no dumb Narcs: you have to be real smart to handle, process and manipulate all this information.

This complex Narc framework is what makes it so tricky to spot one. There is a "real" Personality there, with Slices. But that connects to the Engine only through massive self-injections of Pain. That Pain is so massive, so intense, that it's bearable most of the time, only by living in the fantasy void.

Like the fantasies of PsychoLand, NarcVoid has only the rules that Narc sets. A key difference is that PsychoLand is held up by pillars of iron, resting on concrete. While NarcVoid rests on an ever melting and re-freezing layer of snow over the Engine. PsychoLand is stable: NarcVoid is unstable.

That's why you're never sure what you're gonna get with Narc: gushing intense praise; or violating, undermining insult. Narc doesn't know either. Narc is reacting to a very unstable inner world: and acting out from it.

We can't Control and we can't Cure NPD-based acting out.

Suicidal Ideation

As we explained in Chapter 7 of *I Want To Love But*:[14]

---

[14] The Author (2019)

Psycho and Narc both live in Fantasy:

- for Psycho, completely displacing Emotion-grounded Personality
- for Narc, as the only way that Personality can deal with Thoughts & Feelings

They share a trait of being persons in extreme Pain. But how that Pain functions within them is completely different.

We could try to look at how Psycho and Narc relate to the *5 Slices*. The problem is that they really just don't. The Pain has such squishing effect on the normal relationship between Engine Room and *Me Space*. They live through Shadow Slices:

Living in Shadow Slices

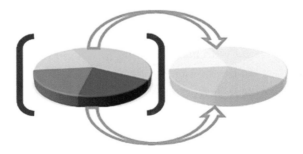

There are no rules about what materials are used to create Shadow Slices. It's different with every Psycho and Narc. What happens when no or low Shadow Slice stuff can escape the Pain barrier is:

The Suicide Trap

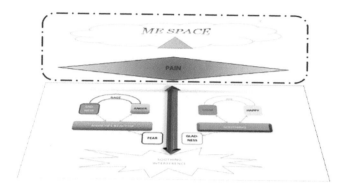

This is what happens when a person stops hearing the music of the *Anxiety-Soothing* dance.

The Sufferer is so immersed in Pain that Pain becomes a prison. There's no way out, because Sufferer is building the bars. The bars are Pain, built to escape the Pain felt from the operation of the Engine Room.

Psycho is not a suicide risk: so long as Psycho can indulge fantasies in PsychoLand. Once deprived of that ability (by jail or asylum) then suicide can become a risk. The inability to act out Fantasies can lead Psycho to conclude that PsychoLand is not in fact real. Or simply become so hopeless that PsychoLand will never be enjoyed again.

We sometimes look at Psycho behaviour as

"suicidal". Psycho takes risks in the real world that we would never consider. But this is not a death wish. In PsychoLand, it is Psycho who makes the rules. Including that bags of skin objects are too stupid for Psycho ever to get caught. And if Psycho does get caught, it's a good opportunity to show bags of skin objects how stupid they were.

A similar dynamic can apply to Narc. The Narc version of hostage-taking at knife point is Gaslighting: telling You lies, that everybody knows are lies and trying to manipulate You to accept them as truth, or to admit you're too stupid to see the truth.

That is very risky behaviour. Truth is an emotional negotiation between people. To terminate this ongoing negotiation blatantly, is to risk termination of the victim's willingness to continue. Gaslighting can get the victim to retreat towards pre-7YO dream space. It's like being abused by a parent. But that's an intolerable place to be, once your adult Self has formed around your core 7YO personality. The Gaslighter is trying to interfere with your *Anxiety-Soothing Rhythm*. The perfect mechanism you were born with can be seriously messed around with pre-7YO. But after that, with your Adult Self protecting it, Narc's interference can't last for long. Your *Anxiety-Soothing Rhythm* will reassert its power: and You're gone.

We can't Control and we can't Cure acting out that is grounded in these pathologies.

What we can do is:
- control ourselves.
- control our own circumstances.
- negotiate with the addict from a position of strength.

These all need us to be able to live in the experience of distance: detachment. To treat the sufferer and their situation like a professional would. This is sometimes called "hard love". It is hard. But the addict responds only to strength, not weakness. Kindness comes from clarity: not confusion.

Scenario
The Client self-reports wanting to feel able to detach from a relationship with an addict, while still being able to offer appropriate support.

Healing

PART 1 CONNECTION

Step 1
1.   You can sit down, or stand. Whatever works for you.
2.   Look at an object or a photo. Anything that reminds you of your connection with the addict.
3.   Close your eyes.
4.   Go inside your head.
5.   Feel whatever feelings come from thinking about that connection.

PART 2 ANXIETY

Step 1

1.   Find some alone space.

2.   Sit down anywhere comfortable.

3.   Take the top two fingers of whatever is your
       writing hand.

4.   Place those fingers gently on the waist side
       of your tummy. (You can find the location
       simply by placing your two fingers over your
       belly button, then moving them around to your
       writing hand side).

5.   Rest your fingers at that spot.

6.   Close your eyes.

7.   Breathe normally.

Step 2

1.   Take the top two fingers of your other hand.

2.   Place them gently at the back of your neck, on
       the other side of your body from your other
       fingers. (Location is anywhere between the nape
       of your neck and your collar-bone: just
       gently move your fingers till you find a spot that
       feels fine to you).

3.   Breathe normally.

Step 3: Take 1 to 2 Minutes

1.   Feel a connection between your fingers.

2.   A connection running through your upper body.
       Like a wire.

3.   You may feel it hot. You may feel it cold.

4.   If it's a hot connection, allow it to get hotter. If it's a cold connection, allow it to get colder.

5.   Allow the connection to become more intense.

6.   Feel it like the filament in a light bulb, getting brighter as you turn up the voltage.

7.   Allow yourself to allow those toxic energy feelings to run through that connection.

8.   Between your fingers, it feels like angry electric ants scurrying around.

9.   It feels like the connection is becoming barbed wire, spilling toxic chemicals into your body.

10.   Let the angry energy become more intense.

11.   And more. Filling your chest and your head.

Step 4

1.   Now it's coursing through you. That toxic writhing energy.

2.   Take the hand with the fingers which are at your waist.

3.   Take the palm of that hand.

4.   Place it gently over the centre of your chest.

5.   Still feel the angry toxic energy coursing through you.

Step 5

1.   Now, you're going in a few moments to take a huge breath in.

2.   Through your nose or your mouth.

3. However you'd do it if you were about to jump into a swimming pool.
4. Big breath in: *Now*.
5. Hold that breath for 3 long seconds.
6. One … Two … Three…
7. Let it out, and at the same time, press your palm into your chest.
8. You can fall back into your chair, or into a lying position, if you like.
9. Rest. Breathe normally.
10. Think whatever thoughts you think. Feel what ever feelings you feel.

End.

PART 3 DISTANCE

Step 1
1. Look again at that object or a photo from Part 1.
2. Close your eyes.
3. Go inside your head.
4. Feel whatever feelings come from thinking about that connection.

Step 2
1. Feel a connection, in your head, with Second You: You.
2. This is just you: yourself, looking at you.
3. You2 is a few arm-lengths away. Like they're standing at the other side of whatever

room you're in.

4.   Allow You₂'s head to connect with yours.

Step 3

1.   You₂ can see your head.
2.   You₂ can see you looking at the object.
3.   You₂ can see the space between you and the object: the distance between you and the object.

Step 4

1.   Feel a connection: between You2 and you.
2.   Feel You₂ watching you.
3.   Feel You₂ watching you, as you look at the object.
4.   Feel You₂ feeling the space between you and the object: the distance between you and the object.

Step 5

1.   You2 can see your head.
2.   You2 can see you looking at the object.
3.   You2 can see the space between you and the object: the distance between you and the object.
        Step 6
1.   Now: reach out, and put those feelings you used to have into the object.
2.   OK: relax.
3.   Now: try again.
4.   You can't find those feelings, or they are vague. That's OK.

5.   Now: try again to put those feelings you used to
        have into the object.

Step 7

1.   OK: relax
2.   Open your eyes.
3.   Breathe.

Step 8

1.   Breathe again: just normally.
2.   Close your eyes.
3.   Think of a happy memory: from when you were
        5-7. Anything happy, big or small.
4.   Now, think of a happy memory: from when you
        were 11-13. Anything happy, big or small.
5.   And, think of a happy memory: from when you
        were 15-17. Anything happy, big or small.
6.   Just let the happy memories swirl around, like
        different flavours of ice cream, in a tub.

Step 9

1.   Now: back to the object.
2.   Try again to put those feelings you used to have:
        into the object
3.   All you're getting back is "ice cream" swirl
        memories. That's fine.
4.   Open your eyes.
5.   Relax.

                            End.

PART 4 BALANCE

Step 1

1.   Find some alone space.
2.   Sit down anywhere comfortable.
3.   Allow yourself to feel as jittery as you often do.

Step 2

1.   Take the palm of your writing hand.
2.   Place it over your tummy: just where your tum
        my button is.
3.   Make sure to leave a little gap between your
        palm and your tummy. This is really important.
        The gap should be a finger-width.
4.   Close your eyes now.
5.   Focus on breathing in through the palm of your hand.
6.   Feel yourself drawing in breaths, through the
        palm of your hand.
7.   Remember how when you were inside your
        mummy, that's where your life support
        came into your body.
8.   You can breathe deep or shallow. Slow or fast.
        Whatever works.

Step 3

1.   Your eyes are still closed.
2.   Take the palm of your other hand.
3.   Place it over your chest.
4.   Make sure to leave a little gap between your
        palm and your chest. This is really important.

       The gap should be a finger-width.

5.   Focus on breathing out through the palm of your hand.

6.   Feel yourself pushing out breaths, through the palm of your hand.

7.   Just do this for as long as you feel you like it.

End.

Explaining

We are using a combination of *Biomorphics* and *Psychotectics*, to gain you distance from the feelings you used to generate around thoughts of the addict and their situation.

We insert the "ice cream" memory feelings so that the detachment is not hostile, but warm.

Part of the problem is that we give ourselves false memories. False in the sense that they bear little relationship to past (or present) reality. We then weaponise them – against ourselves – to create problems in thinking about things that are impossible to solve.

We actually want that impossibility. We want to try avoiding solution of the real problems, because that involves us making hard choices. To keep all these plates spinning we need energy. We steal that energy by repressing our Anxiety. Which leaves us exhausted.

In a way, we end up mirroring the psychopathy and NPD of the addict. We actually start matching their thinking (or what we think it is), with our own. It's a classic predator defence response in nature. But it's not so useful in urban family and relationship life experience.

These paths are all journeys to losing ourselves. To weakness and dependence. The pathways of the addict, not the detached carer.

After Care
We can gain instant relief from this *Healing*. But the cause of what troubles us keeps repeating. That propels us to re-invent those insoluble problems, as out defence mechanism.

So we will need to repeat this *Healing*. It's free. It takes a few minutes. It works. So that's three up on trying to deal with these heart-rending problems the other way.

CHAPTER 8

CHILD LINES

A really fun and exciting use of Matrixial Therapy is in changing how children read and write and play music. We can also help to provide emotional balance: but only gently and within the child's own limits.

The Recipes work well with children under the age of 7. The bottom of the age range tends to be around 3. Really, as soon as a child is able to hold a pencil, and recognise letter shapes and sounds.

We know that the Recipes work, both from scientific experiment, and from teacher experience.

We explain the theory in Chapter 6 of *The Matrixial Brain: Experiments in Reality*.

> The Theory
> The Self Systems Architecture is comprised of an /S/ continuum of /S/ubjectivity "sandwiched" between operant interfaces of Objectivity:[15]

---

[15] see *Secret Self*, Chapters 2 and 3 (2020); and see Part 1 *Healing How*

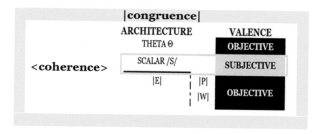

The Theta Θ field interacts Ю with ।W।orld objectively. That Ю interaction has effect upon our ।P।hysiology. ।P। responds to virtualised inputs, whether from ।W।, or Ю.

Objective Interface Writing
The Proposition is that we can can alter Ю, by Mimetic effect in Θ, generating by a person outside the Self.

In earlier Chapters we have seen exploration of the ।W। -/S/ - Θ interfaces. We have tested and validated our ability to create interventions which significantly influence accord and discord between /S/ and Θ.

We have tested and validated our ability to create interventions which significantly alter /S/<coherence>. Our understanding of the Self Systems Architecture and the dynamics of its interactive processes, provides us with Psychotectic theory.

This enables us to construct Congruence Interface Therapy (CIT) interventions. We can use Avatar techniques (You$_2$), to engage Θ<Constructs>.

We predict the validity of *CIT Spatial Morphonics*: that we can use these as ЮIWI interfaces, to change your spatial motor interaction with the external world.

Chapter 6 of *The Matrixial Brain* sets out the experimental results:

I-Pen

We tasked 3 repetitions of this Scene across all 3 Sets. This was because, given the uniqueness of the IMI entation experience involved, it was important to set control parameters, by cross-Set tasking.

We set up, with these simple task directions:

(12) Experiment: I-Pen

Step 1:
Prologue:
You must use whatever is your non-ordinary writing hand, in this experience.
- If you are right-handed, use your left. Your You$_2$ will come from your right.
- If you are left-handed, use your right. Your You$_2$ will come from your left.

Materials:
Get a pad of paper, limed or unlined
Get a ballpoint pen (because it writes most clearly and easily)

Part 1:
• With your normal writing hand, write on the pad: A B C
• Do it with reasonable care and concentration. Not slapdash
Stop

Part 2:
• With your Other hand, write on the pad: A B C
• Do it best you can. Take your time

Then, we engage the You$_2$ avatar:

Part 3:
Imagine a second you. A perfect replica copy of you. This is secondYou: You$_2$

For this *Experiment*:
- imagine you're on a tennis court
- with the room at the other end
- and You$_2$ where the umpire would be
- on your right-hand side (your left-hand side, if you're left-handed)

imagine You$_2$ looking at You and the pen and paper
You$_2$ can see You
You$_2$ can see inside Your head
You$_2$ can move the hand and pen on the paper

Feel the connection with You$_2$
Move yourself out of your head
Allow You$_2$ to move the hand and pen on the paper

Then the Test instruction:

Now:
(1)   With your Other hand: write on the pad: A B C

Keep your You$_2$ connection going all the time
Write slowly. Allow You$_2$ to move the hand and pen on the paper
Do it best you can. Take your time

We are moments after Parts 1 and 2 of the Test. Nothing of significance has changed in the environmental reality or Self state of the respondents: except their engagement of the You$_2$ avatar.

If the Proposition is invalid, then we should find a zero or near zero alteration in motor-graphic skills.

Step 1: Response (1)	12.1
PROPOSITION: At Part 2, the quality of my other hand writing, compared to normal hand writing was below 30%	MARK
A Agree	
B Disagree	
C Not Sure	

Step 1: Response (2)	12.2
PROPOSITION: With You2 the quality of my other hand writing, compared to normal hand was 80% or above	MARK
A Agree	
B Disagree	
C Not Sure	

What we find is a range $\sum R$ values, across 3 Sets of 30 Respondents each, spread randomly across the UK, which are far away from =0:

RESULT

TEST	%			
	S1	**S2**	**S3**	**S4**
I-Pen (1)	60	40		
I-Pen (2)	77	40		
I-Pen (3)	67	37		

The Proposition is validated.

Not by mere self-reporting of what appears to be going on in one's head. But by factual graphic data in the real world, which can be ascertained and measured objectively.

We deliberately set the achievement threshold very high, at 80%, so as to benchmark validation as firmly as reasonably possible. It's a fair inference, that lower benchmarks, set at say 60% or 30% improvement, would have yielded even higher $\sum R$ values.

Annex A to *The Matrixial Brain* sets out statistical analyses by Fabian Goguta:

> The nonparametric McNemar test was used to test whether the differences in answers to the first question given in Step 1 and at Step 2 were statistically significant.
>
> Conclusion
>
> The test showed that the intervention produced a statistically significant change in answers ($p = .003$)

We first tested this I-Pen technique with adults. In *Matrixial Logic*, Chapter 5, we provided some real-world examples of how Subjects are able to use the You_2 avatar in I-Pen. These were all done simply by the Practitioner guiding the Subject orally over the phone.

It's useful to see how adult writing skills improve, using I-Pen:

Here is a sample:[16]

Normal Hand

Unassisted
Other Hand

You_2
Other Hand

---

[16] by a friend of the Author

and, in a second round of practice, a few moments later:

Normal Hand

You₂
Other Hand

Another sample from a different individual:

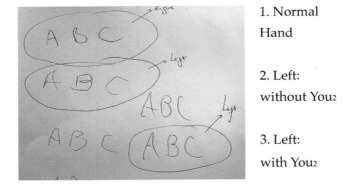

1. Normal Hand

2. Left: without You₂

3. Left: with You₂

The 3ʳᵈ writing was performed moments after the 2ⁿᵈ writing.

More samples:

(3)

1. Normal hand

2. Left: without You₂

3.1 Left: without You₂

3.3 Left: with You₂

(4)

1. Left: without You₂

1.1 Left: without You₂

2. Left: with You₂

2.1 Left: with You₂

(5)

1. Normal hand

2. Left: without You₂

3.1 Left: with You₂

3.2 Left: with You₂

3.3 Left: with You₂

The same theory works, in improving child reading skills, as we'll see in a moment.

One of the exciting aspects of writing therapy, is that it's *really* real. Of course, you know if your headache has gone, or your pain has gone away. But nobody else does. What's different with these uses of *Matrixial Science,* is that you can actually see – there in the real world – physical proof that the Recipe is working.

26.   Perfect Handwriting

It takes until around age 7 for a child to develop an independent, fully-functioning personality. It's no accident that, right across history, serious child schooling has started at this age. For example the Spartans (these guys):

https://medium.com/@vogt.ben/the-amazing-300-72a6fa6d63c5

were sent to their special training school after their 7th birthday. It's at age 7 (ish) that we become the person who we're going to be for the rest of our lives. That's like our basic frame of personality, and everything else is built on top of it.

Understanding this is really important when it comes to using *Matrixial Therapy* with a child under that age. Before 7, a child is just working out how to me an I and a Me: how to have a sense of Self.

In other Chapters of this book, we're using *Psychotectics*. We use the You2 Avatar as a way of connecting across a bridge between the thinking / feeling brain, and the "computer" brain.

Now, that won't work with kids, because they are still working out what it is to be a "You 1". The younger the child is, the more difficult it would be for them to think of a second "Me". So, we have to adjust the Recipes.

But, in a way, their child-mind makes this even easier than with a grown up. You'll already know that children have a wonderful make-believe mind. Kids are happy to believe that Santa Claus and fairies and all things wonderful really exist.
So do we, in fact. We just make up better stories about why the things in our head are really out there in the world. And, we use a different set of brain processes for doing it.

So, it really is "child's play" for kids to use an invisible friend to help them do things.

That's how we make these Recipes work. We need to think about having these conversations around the Recipes. Let's call the teacher or parent or practitioner "Adult":

> Version 1:
>
> Adult: Hey, so, do you have an invisible friend?
>
> Child: Yes.
>
> Adult: Cool! What are they like?
>
> Child: [tells their idea]
>
> Adult: That's great. So, can you talk with [name of invisible friend] now?
>
> Child: Yes.
>
> or
>
> Child: No.
>
> Adult: OK, can you get [name of invisible friend] to come be here with you now?
>
> Child: OK.
>
> Adult: Great! So, we're going to ask [name of invisible friend] to do some writing for you. Is that cool?
>
> Child: Yaay.
>
> Version 2:
>
> Adult: If you had a special invisible friend, what would it be?
>
> Child: Hmmm...

Adult:	A unicorn? A monkey? A dinosaur?[17]
Child:	Unicorn!
Adult:	Yaay. OK. What colour is Unicorn?
Child:	Pink.
Adult:	Aww. And is Unicorn all pink, or with spots?
Child:	Spots.
Adult:	Wow, what colour spots?
Child:	Yellow ones.
Adult:	Ooh. Big ones or small ones?
Child:	Big ones.

The colours and spots talk helps to get the Child to "invest" in the Avatar. To sense the Avatar as a real presence there in the room with them. This is important for the Steps.

Adult:	OK, can you get Unicorn to come be here with you now?
Child:	OK.
Adult:	Great! So, we're going to ask Unicorn to do some writing for you. Is that cool?
Child:	Yaay.

Making Contact:

| Adult: | Can you close your eyes and say 'Hello' to [name of invisible friend]? |
| Child: | OK. |

17 these tend to be very popular

Adult:	Yaay. Can [name of invisible friend] say 'Hello' to you?
Child:	Mmm hmmm.
Adult:	Yaay.

We can also help with making contact, by getting Child to give the Avatar a make-believe Present. Then getting Unicorn to do the same for Child. This is about getting the Child to really sense a linkage between Child and Avatar.

These conversations are just general guides. Every child is different. It's all about seeing the world from the child's point of view: helping to guide them to the connection with what in the adult world we call "You2": the Avatar.

There's no point in rushing this stage. Without that Avatar connection becoming firmly established, the Recipe won't work.

The child has a "computer" brain, just like adults do. It works *just the same*. But it has fewer "programs". Programs that the child "computer" brain definitely does have, are *shape recognition* patterns. We are born with these. That's how a baby who is just a few hours old actually recognises mum.

A 3 year old child can recognise triangles, circles and squares as different. So can a baby who is just a few months old. Just think how amazing that actually is. A

258

child can use the same "computer" brain program for the letter shapes of the Western alphabet.

That's what they are made up from. Combinations of:
<blockquote>
lines |
triangles   Δ
circles   O
</blockquote>

The letter A: a triangle with 2 lines added. The letter V: the same lines, without the triangle.
The letter B: a line with 2 semi-circles.
The letter C: half a circle.

So, all we need to do is to connect this *shape recognition* program in the "computer" brain, to what the writing hand needs to do.

Scenario
We're going to help to improve the writing of a child aged 3 to 7.

Healing
These Steps are spoken to the Child writer.

The Child, we assume, is already sitting down with their pen and paper. The paper can be lined or unlined.

You don't need to have an example A B C in front of the Child. In fact, this can be distracting. The Child's "computer" brain already knows these shapes.

Step 1

1.   Let's write our A B C in nice big letters.
2.   [Child writes: it's all wobbly]
3.   Yaay ! [encouragement words]

Step 2

1.   Now, let's get Unicorn to sit by your shoulder.
2.   Give Unicorn a stroke with your hand.

Step 3

1.   OK. Now you can let Unicorn guide your
         writing hand.
2.   Let your hand feel a little tingle.
3.   As Unicorn gets in touch with your writing hand.
4.   Let your fingers feel a little tingle.
5.   As Unicorn gets in touch with your fingers.

Step 4

1.   Let Unicorn move your writing hand.
2.   So Unicorn can help you draw a Line in the air.
3.   [Child draws]. Yaay!
4.   Let Unicorn move your writing hand.
5.   So Unicorn can help you draw a Circle in the air.
6.   [Child draws]. Yaay!
7.   Let Unicorn move your writing hand.
8.   So Unicorn can help you draw a Triangle in the
         air.

9.   [Child draws]. Yaay!

Step 5

1.   Now Unicorn can do your writing for you: Yaay!
2.   Put your writing hand on the paper, so it's ready for Unicorn.

Step 6

1.   Let Unicorn write your big letters A B C for you.
2.   You can close your eyes if it helps.
3.   Just like drawing the Line, and the Circle and the Triangle.

Step 7

1.   So, you can just stroke Unicorn.
2.   While Unicorn writes your A B C for you.
3.   There you go: A... B... C...

Step 8

1.   Amazing! Look!
2.   It's so good.
3.   You and your Unicorn: what an amazing team!

End.

Explaining

The key is, of course, helping the Child to use the "Unicorn" Avatar. Step 4 is a big help with this. The Child is able to draw the shapes, in the air. This step away from the writing paper, allows the Child to feel the Avatar connection, without the circumstantial pressure of actual writing.

We do the capital letters A B C for a number of reasons:

- these are easier letters to form than lower case: a b c
- the Child can focus on shapes, without having to worry about actual words.

Let's just look at that last point. In *Matrixial Logic*, Chapter 5, we explained how name words (nouns: words for things) are held in our subjective mind. The structure of language (grammar, syntax) is held in our "computer" brain.

So, when we want to focus the Child on letter shapes – which are also held in our "computer" brain – we want to keep away from using the subjective mind, as much as we can.

When we ask young children to write sentences about things, we are asking them to do something really complicated:

- use the shapes in their "computer" brain.
- use name words in their thinking/feeling brain.

- wrap them together in grammatical structures,
  which are also in their "computer" brain.

No wonder children struggle for years with this. The *Matrixial Brain Experiments* show that adult brains also find lots of thought creations impossible: *how we can think limits what we can think.*

So, the next step in Child writing is to do the lower case a b c. Then to work through the other letters of the alphabet. Using triplets of letters works well, with a child's concentration level.

What we want to achieve with this is *automation*. So that, the moment the Child picks up the pen, the Child automatically switches on the Avatar connection. This does happen, The Child wants it to happen, because every child likes doing well. The Avatar allows the Child to succeed. It is an active friend.

After Care

The next step is getting the Child to copy collections of words. What we are actually doing here, is getting the Child to write words made of shapes. Grammar is irrelevant.

Examples of Avatar writing with children around 4 years old:

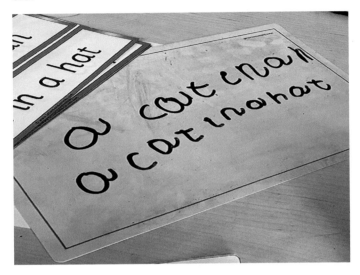

2nd lines using Unicorn Avatar

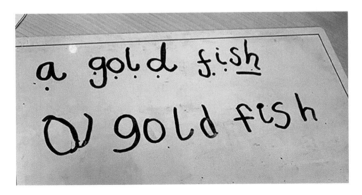

Top line is Teacher

Top line is Teacher

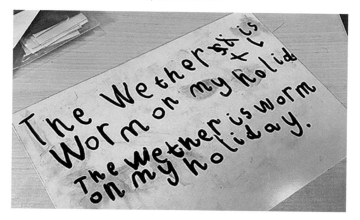

Taking the Child into learning grammar can use the Avatar method as well. What we need to remember here is that different parts of the brain Architecture do different things.

Words for things and their meaning, are held in the thinking/feeling brain. The rules of how words are put together – grammar – is held in the "computer" brain. We ask too much of the average kindergarten kid to use both of these different parts of the brain, at the same time.

So, with Matrixial learning, what we do is allow the different parts of the Child's brain to learn differently.

Step 1 is something everyone does: show the Child the picture and the name word.

Dog

Sheep

Step 2 is to get across the idea of a Verb: the doing word. This is part of *Syntax*: the rules of how sentences work. These words have no meaning, in themselves. They are just made-up, in a way that names of things words aren't.

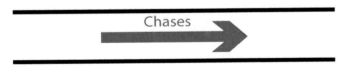

Chases

We can show the Child pictures and videos of running towards and running away from. They get the idea. The point is: *to leave that idea in the "computer" brain.*

The final step comes in putting it together:

The way we do this, is to blank out the words, and *just use the pictures and symbol*. These shapes are, of course also held in the "computer" brain. The Child can put the *meanings* of the images together, without using the words.

And – believe it or not – that's exactly how you, the adult, do it as well.

The final Step is *translation*. This is a two-part Step. First, we get the Child to translate the pictures into words:

Dog   Chases   Sheep

The second part is getting the Child to see how the "chases" changes the Dog and Sheep. This is what the different colours mean:

Dog

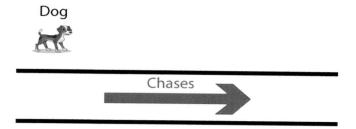

Dog

The **Black** Dog is just there, not doing anything.
The **Green** Dog is doing Chase. Similarly with the Sheep.

And you guessed it, the Colours are in our "computer" brain, as well.

We can use the Avatar to help with all this. It's good to do that, as that Avatar will be really important when we come to getting the Child's reading age up.

27.   Reading Age Up

The first thing we need to understand, is that reading aloud is a completely different brain exercise to reading silently, to oneself.

Reading aloud uses the "computer" brain, to interact with the outside world (even if nobody else is listening). Reading to oneself, uses the thinking/feeling part of the brain.

You don't believe us? OK: you read the first sentence in the paragraph above *aloud*; then the second sentence to yourself.

Now, review the history of your head. You'll notice that, when reading aloud, your eyes look at the words very differently, to how you read to yourself. This is part of the difference between the two processes.

So, in getting a child's reading age up, we need to practice reading *aloud*.

Scenario
We want to improve the reading age of a Child aged 3 to 7.

Set the Child up with a storybook. The Child can sit on your knee or near you.

Healing
Step 1

1.   OK, let's do some reading aloud.
2.   Allow Child to read aloud.
3.   Yaay! [encouragement words]

Step 2

1.   Now, let's get Unicorn to sit by your shoulder.
2.   Give Unicorn a stroke with your hand.

Step 3

1.   OK. Now you can let Unicorn do your reading for you.
2.   Let Unicorn see through your eyes, and Unicorn will do the reading.
3.   Just listen to the words Unicorn gives you.
4.   Allow Child to read aloud.

Step 4
1.   Yaay! That's so good.
2.   You and your Unicorn: what an amazing team!

End.

Explaining

From these simple Steps, it may not be easy to imagine the amazing outcome. We've seen children stumbling with their reading. The child connects with the Avatar. Their reading picks up pace and becomes clearer. Suddenly, they're rattling through the reading.

After Care

Especially for younger kids, the Avatar connection needs practice. It's just getting them into the habit of using the Unicorn – or whatever - to do their reading for them. They love to do it, because they get instant results: and we all like instant!

In case you were wondering, this doesn't create a bad dependency. It's not like the child needs to start carrying around an actual Unicorn with them, like a comfort blanket. Through practice, the brain "re-wires" its connections.[18] Different children takes different times to learn the same habits in ordinary real life. So, it can takes days or weeks for a child to learn the habit of Avatar connection.

---

[18] there's a whole literature on this.

Once it is learnt: it stays. The connection becomes automatic. The "computer" brain ability becomes integrated with the child's thinking/feeling brain.

Finally, the writing and reading makes each other better. The child can "see" better the shapes they're reading, and the words they are writing.

28. *Mini Music*

Children hear and recognise tunes effortlessly. When we put two or more children together to play music, even simple tapping of a xylophone and tambourine, what do we notice? *That children have problems with rhythm.*

A child has their own individual rhythm. Or rather, changing rhythms: changing with the thoughts and feelings going on from moment to moment in the child's subjective brain.

PART 1 RHYTHYM

We can actually get children to keep time with an outside beat. Even more amazingly, we can get children to keep that beat *in their own heads*.

We explain the theory in Chapter 6 of *The Matrixial Brain*. If the reader wishes to skip the theory and go straight into the *Scenario* and *Healing*, that's fine. Using the Recipe will show, sure enough, to the reader, that it all really works, in the real world. And you can see it working, as a fact that you can record and measure.

The Theory

We restate the core of Matrixial Science: the Self Systems Architecture is comprised of an /S/ continuum of /S/ubjectivity "sandwiched" between operant interfaces of Objectivity:[19]

The Theta ⊖ field interacts Ю with |W|orld objectively.

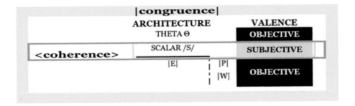

We can now add the final layer, which illustrates the *Chronal Congruence* of ⊖⇔ |W|:

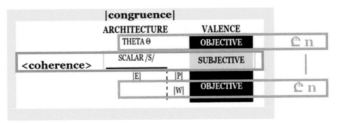

That Ю interaction achieves moment by moment

| congruence | in quantised | T | ime.

Mind Time

The Proposition is that we can can alter Temporal Ю, by Mimetic effect in Θ, generating by a person outside the Self.

In earlier Chapters we have seen exploration of the | W | -/S/ - Θ interfaces. We have tested and validated our ability to create interventions which significantly influence accord and discord between /S/ and Θ.

We have tested and validated our ability to create interventions which significantly alter /S/<coherence>.

Our understanding of the Self Systems Architecture and the dynamics of its interactive processes, provides us with Psychotectic theory.

This enables us to construct *Congruence Interface Therapy* (CIT) interventions. We can use Avatar techniques (You$_2$), to engage Θ<Constructs>.

We have validated the Predictions of *CIT Spatial Morphonics*: that we can use these Ю | W | interfaces, to change your motor-spatial interaction with the external world.

We now Predict the validity of *CIT Temporal Morphonics*: that we can use these IO I W I interfaces, to change your temporal interaction with the external world.

If the Predictions are validated, then I T I ime cannot be the phenomenon described in Newtonian, Einsteinian, or even Quantum accounts. Conceptions of time as a "flow" external to the Self, can no longer operate as a substratum of neuroscience, philosophy or psychology.[20]

The Experiments
The collection of Scenes which are directed principally to exploring *CIT* Temporal Morphonics are:
(1)   Noming (1)
(2)   Noming (2)
(3)   Noming (3)
(4)   [16] Soundspace
(5)   [17] Ropetime
(6)   [57] Timecart

The Results
The Results reveal statistically significant averages which support the Proposition:

---

[20] quantum theories and neuroscience have already begun to move beyond the boundaries of Classical accounts of time.

TEST	RESULT %				
	S1	S2	S3	S4	S5
Noming (1)	20	63	27	67	
Noming (2)	30	73	43	40	
Noming (3)	23	67	80	50	
		47			
[16] Soundspace	60				
[17] Ropetime	47	37			
[57] Timecart	40	43	50	60	47

Noming

We tasked 3 repetitions of this Scene across all 3 Sets. This was because, given the uniqueness of the |M| entation experience involved, it was important to set control parameters, by cross-Set tasking.

We set up the basic wirework:

(13) Experiment: Noming

Preparation:

- Google "30 bpm"
- choose a metronome (YouTube or any will do)
- Make sure the Metronome has a seconds time clock counter
- Be ready to press Play (don't Play yet)

You will then have an audible 30 beats per minute: one beat every 2 seconds.

Test that you can hear the beat.

A 5 Beat takes 10 seconds: check the time from 0.00 on your YouTube clock (your Youtube clock will show 9 seconds of count: that's because the next Beat occurs on the 10th second).

We then run the control test:

Step 1:
- get one finger ready: to tap on the table, or your leg
- play the metronome
- do 5 Beats

(1) try and tap your finger in time with the Beats

From Practice, we know that it's quite hard to achieve beat synchronisation:

Step 1: Response	13.1
PROPOSITION: I find it difficult to match the beats	MARK
A Agree	
B Disagree	
C Not Sure	

RESULT

TEST	%				
	S1	S2	S3	S4	S5
Noming (1)	20				
Noming (2)	30				
Noming (3)	23				

Based on Practice experience, we suspect some under-reporting here.

Then, we engage the You$_2$ avatar:

Step 2:
Same Preparation as Step 1
Close your eyes and focus

Imagine a second you. A perfect replica copy of you. This is secondYou: You$_2$

Feel You$_2$ hovering to one side of your shoulder or the other

Then the Test instruction:

imagine You$_2$
looking at You and
seeing the space between the Beats
You$_2$ can see You
You$_2$ can see inside Your head
You$_2$ can move your finger with the Beats

Now:
- get one finger ready: to tap on the table, or your leg
- play the metronome
- do 5 Beats
- (1) tap your finger in time with the Beats

We are moments after Step 1 of the Test. Nothing of significance has changed in the environmental reality or Self state of the respondents: except their engagement of the You$_2$ avatar.

If the Proposition is invalid, then we should find a zero or near zero alteration in temporal synchronisation skills.

Step 2: Response (1)		13.2
PROPOSITION: Now it's easy to match the beats		MARK
A	Agree	
B	Disagree	
C	Not Sure	

What we find is a range $\sum R$ values, across 3 Sets of 30 Respondents each, spread randomly across the UK, which are far away from $=0$:

TEST	RESULT %				
	S1	S2	S3	S4	S5
Noming (1)	20	63			
Noming (2)	30	73			
Noming (3)	23	67			

The Proposition is validated.

Not by mere self-reporting of what appears to be going on in one's head. But by factual graphic data in the real world, which can be ascertained and measured objectively.

In this Test structure, there was no external observer, or bear sensing apparatus. We can reasonably infer that Respondents were being truthful and accurate in their self-reporting of *externally* manifested events.

Step 2: Response (2)	13.3
PROPOSITION: It's like someone else is tapping the beats for me	MARK
A	Agree	
B	Disagree	
C	Not Sure	

We were interested to see if Respondents felt and a specific /S/ relationship to the avatar experience:

This question revealed a wide range of $\sum R$ values:

TEST	RESULT %				
	S1	S2	S3	S4	S5
Noming (1)			27		
Noming (2)			43		
Noming (3)			80		

There appears to be no convergence between S2 and S3. This diffusion of response is interesting, in illuminating the subjective self-reporting of Respondents' experiences. It is peripheral to the Proposition Predictions.

We then invoke a real world manifestation of extraordinary synchrony. We turn the metronome sound off: and test whether Respondents can still keep time with the external beat:

And: ***turn the metronome sound off***

You're going to:
- play the metronome, ***silently***
- Make the 1st Beat the same time as you press Play
- tap your finger in time with the Beats
- for 5 Beats (9 seconds of time)

Then Press Stop [spacebar or mouse] on the 5th beat

We provide the concluding instruction:

Now:
Close your eyes and focus
(1) Press Play and Tap the 1st Beat
(2) Beat 4 more times
(3) Press stop on the 4th Beat

And: check that the YouTube clock counter read 9 Seconds

We know from Practice experience, that the acceptance of /S/ <coherence> narrow-banding takes some practice. The more that /S/ interferes, the worse the result is. So we directed:

Please practice up to 3 times and then give your final answer

If the Proposition is invalid, then we should find a zero or near zero alteration in temporal synchronisation skills.

Step 3: Response	13.4
PROPOSITION:	MARK
The YouTube clock counter does read 9 Seconds	
A Agree	
B Disagree	
C Not Sure	

What we find is a range $\sum R$ values, across 3 Sets of 30 Respondents each, spread randomly across the UK, which are far away from =0:

			RESULT		
TEST			**%**		
	S1	**S2**	**S3**	**S4**	**S5**
Noming (1)				67	
Noming (2)				40	
Noming (3)				50	

The Proposition is validated.

Not by mere self-reporting of what appears to be going on in one's head. But by factual graphic data in the real world, which can be ascertained and measured objectively.

Averaged across Set groups, we find $\sum R = 52\%$. A clear majority of these Sets were able radically to alter their temporal interface with the real world, under the techniques directed by Matrixial Science.

Now, let's make some mini music rhythm.

Scenario

A child, or indeed adult, wants to be able to play an instrument to a beat, without having an external time-keeper.

28A   Rhythm Healing

Step 1

1.   Get comfortable with your instrument.
        Whatever works for you.
2.   Get a beat track: from Google or a metronome.
3.   Set it to the beat you'd like to keep: the External
        Beat.

Step 2

1.   Turn on the External Beat.
2.   Play along to the beat for a few beats.
3.   Do the best you can to follow the beat.
4.   Turn off the External Beat.
5.   Relax.

Step 3

1.   Now, close your eyes.

2. Feel a connection, in your head, with Second You: You$_2$.[21]
3. This is just you: yourself, looking at you.
4. You$_2$ is just by your shoulder.
5. Allow You$_2$'s head to connect with yours.

Step 4

1. Allow You$_2$ to connect to the hand which is your rhythm hand on the instrument.
2. Allow You$_2$ to feel through your hand to your fingers.

Step 5

1. Turn on the External Beat.
2. Play along to the beat for a few beats.
3. Do the best you can to follow the beat.
4. Turn off the External Beat.
5. Relax

This time, playing with the External Beat was much easier. Practice this a few times. Keep the You$_2$ connection going.

Step 6

1. Relax
2. Close your eyes.
3. Feel the You$_2$ connection to your rhythm hand

---

[21] Remember that, for children under 7, this is best done as an Invisible friend": usually an animal or imaginary creature

and fingers.

4. Feel You₂ counting the beats for you, which match the External Beat.

5. Open your eyes if you like.

6. Ready: Play!

End.

Explaining

You'll be able to play to an external time (like in the *Noming* Experiment), and see that you're keeping perfect time. You can record your playing rhythm and prove it.

After Care

This one is all about practice. Not so much practice at how the connection with You₂ works: that's instant and amazing.

It's practice at gaining that connection. This is just a matter of repetition. You can do that practice without the instrument. Just concentrate for a few moments and tap in time with that External Beat.

Of course, you can develop a collection of External Beats. Most Western music, especially pop/rock, is written in beats per minute of 120, 132, and 156. Loud and live can get up to 162 even as fast as 172. The point is, there's a very limited number of External Beats to learn.

PART 2 TONES

Tuning a stringed instrument is tricky. When you play a piano, guitar or violin, each tone doesn't produce a single sound. What you actually get is a layering of sounds, with one as the dominant. That dominant is how we describe the tone: say A sharp.

That's why it's hard to tune these instruments: whether to a tuning fork or a keyboard, or synthesized sound.

The dominant tones have a spatial relationship in a soundscape. That landscape is how we construct scales.

Another amazing effect of using the "computer" brain, is that it recognises that soundscape, as a series of sound "shapes". What to the subjective (thinking, feeling) brain is fuzzy, to the "computer" brain is clear.

Scenario
A child, or indeed adult, wants to be able to tune an instrument.

28B   *Tone Healing*
Step 1
1.   Get comfortable with your instrument.
        Whatever works for you.
2.   Get your reference tone-setter ready.

Step 2

1.   Now, close your eyes.
2.   Feel a connection, in your head, with Second
       You: You$_2$.
3.   This is just you: yourself, looking at you.
4.   You$_2$ is just by your shoulder.
5.   Allow You$_2$'s head to connect with yours.

Step 3

1.   Allow You$_2$ to connect to the hand which is your
       playing hand on the instrument.
2.   Allow You$_2$ to feel through your hand to your
       fingers.

Step 4

1.   Play your reference tone.
2.   Hear it though You$_2$.
3.   Play your instrument string.
4.   Hear it though You$_2$.
5.   You$_2$ will automatically calculate difference
       between the 2 tones.

Step 5

1.   Adjust your string.
2.   Play again.
3.   Repeat Step 4.

End.

Explaining

There's not much more to explain than with Part 1: unless we want to dive into complicated audio-neural territory.

After Care

Again, this will get better with repetition.

What you'll find over the days to come is that you can "hear" through your "computer" brain those perfect tones.

CHAPTER 9

LEARNING DIFFICULTIES

The journey from new-born to adult is not easy, with the best of circumstances. Every child finds difficulty in achieving emotional balance. Indeed, that imbalance is perhaps what most characterises the child.

We don't want to change that. What we want is to provide the child with more control, in the sense of being able to get into a state of emotional balance when they need or want it.

Learning difficulties arising from Dyslexia or Autism (and they can overlap), are distressing for child, parent and teacher. *Matrixial Science* helps to explain the origin and processes of these problems.

Matrixial Healing can help to show the child hope. Rainbows in the understanding of their own abilities to experience the world better. Sunlight in experiencing that understanding more happily. That's perhaps one of the greatest gifts we can share with these amazing kids.

29.   *Emotional Balance*

Until around age 7, children don't fully develop an independent Personality.

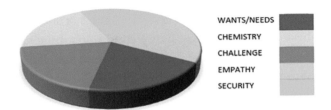

In *Healing How*, we look at the 5 Slices of Personality:

We can see, underlying the different Slices, the momentum of the *ASR* (Anxiety-Soothing Rhythm):

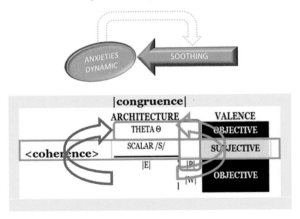

It is our elementary [needs], from birth, which engage the Anxiety reflex. Satisfaction engages our Soothing response: equalised under *Architectural* | congruence |.

With the development of Personality: our thoughts and feelings alter, every moment, the balance between the Slices:

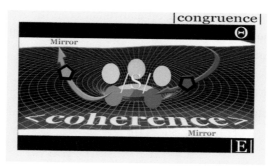

We can trigger our Anxiety, by thinking ideas about our Wants. We can see how Satisfaction signals are part of the Security slice. We have to learn when to start (or accept) a conflict, and when to stop: when matters are Satisfied. When we are not Satisfied (which is always, after a Satisfaction event has passed), we Need or Want: and the Slices Cycle begins again.

The Slices Cycle is how You live your life. Every moment of every day. Your Slices Cycle has been created since your first breath on earth. It is unique to You, in your personality. Yet that cycle demonstrates both continuity over time (which can be marked by discontinuity) and an averaging into the model Slices.

All of this happens under the "gravitational" force of the /S/ continuum: under our innate need for <coherence>. /S/ is illuminated by mirrors. Reflection is the essential process for doing our thinking in /S/.

The process of creating a balance between the 5 Slices of Personality, is what the growth of the child is all about. These are the main Stages:

0 – 18 Months
The newborn to toddler Stage is, in a way similar to our adult use of Shadow Slices Ш:

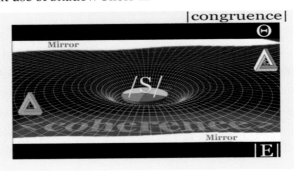

The "impossible triangles" represent Ш Shadow Slices.

During this Stage, we notice things. But we haven't yet got this machinery working:

So, we have ideas of things, which are just scattered. We don't yet have Frames of Reference by which we can think: hmm... this thing is like that thing...so...

Yet, if we look at a child in this stage, the child is looking for "this is like that" all the time. Looking for similarities and differences.

We must remember that the Architecture, and the "computer" brain are both there from birth. The "computer" brain runs basic programs for survival, and works with the Anxiety-Soothing Rhythm. You can imagine the thinking/feeling brain as being "squished", or small, like this:

18 Months to 3 Years
The child passes through the "terrible 2s". This is the time when the child has developed enough of this stuff:

to begin becoming a mini-personality.

From 18 months, the child is connecting their thinking/ feeling brain with the "computer" brain. This is a traumatic time. Achieving stability in those connections is not easy. No other species on earth has to manage it. It seems to be language learning which directs us through this journey.

3 to 7 Years
The machinery is ready. We fill it with information from our childhood experiences. We use the information to create an ever-changing balance (a dynamic harmony) between our 5 Slices.

Where we are, from time to time, influences what we are. What we are affects what we can become. And how we can think (and feel) governs what we can think (and feel).

Scenario
We'd like the Child to get the best out of their learning time. The Child sometimes has problems with keeping an emotional balance. Perhaps being hyper-manic, or isolating. Or swinging from one mood to another.

Now, we need to accept that this is part and parcel of the process of growing. How easy did you find learning to drive? What happens to you when even a little of a mind-altering substance like alcohol starts messing around with your brain circuitry?

So, to expect Victorian-like "perfection" in children is misguided. The swings and roundabouts, snakes and ladders of a child's personality and brain growth are normal and natural.

But we can help the child to get more out of the process, and feel more comfortable with themselves.

This healing is for a parent to do. You don't need any professional practitioner help. Just run the Steps. The Recipe needs the child to follow some basic instructions. So, for kids under 3 years old, it probably won't work.

This can work with individual children, or with a small group of kids. It's just getting them to do Simon Says, with their little hands.

Healing

Step 1

1.   Let's sit down together.
2.   Watch me and copy me: like Simon Says.

Step 2

1.   Take the palm of your writing hand.
2.   Place it over your tummy: just where your tum my button is.

3.   Make sure to leave a little gap between your palm and your tummy. This is really important. The gap should be a finger-width.

4.   You can close your eyes, or keep them open.

5.   Focus on breathing in through the palm of your hand.

6.   Feel yourself drawing in breaths, through the palm of your hand.

7.   Remember how when you were inside your mummy, that's where your life support came into your body.

8.   You can breathe deep or shallow. Slow or fast. Whatever works.

Step 3

1.   You can close your eyes, or keep them open.

2.   Take the palm of your other hand.

3.   Place it over your chest.

4.   Make sure to leave a little gap between your palm and your chest. This is really important. The gap should be a finger-width.

5.   Focus on breathing out through the palm of your hand.

6.   Feel yourself pushing out breaths, through the palm of your hand.

We call Steps 2 and 3 *Angel Wings*.

End.

Explaining

We've seen other uses for *Angel Wings*. What makes this technique so useful for kids is that it only does what their own *Anxiety-Soothing Rhythm* systems allow. It allows:

- better balance
- more peace
- enhanced power

These are all dynamics. They mix up with each other. Much that kids experience teaches them (deliberately or by accident) to repress their Anxiety (and the Soothing which comes with it).

The insight of the Montessori[22] educational system is that kids can be self-motivating in learning. By regimenting them, we undermine their own dynamics of ability. We can argue till the cows come home about whether liberation or regulation work best, and in what mixture.

This simple Angel Wings technique allows kids to get the best out of both, by getting the best out of themselves.

After Care

A 3 year old can learn *Angel Wings* after just a few repetitions. It's just two simple hand positions. The changes in breathing and in the *Anxiety-Soothing Rhythm* happen automatically.

---

[22] https://en.wikipedia.org/wiki/Montessori_education

It feels nice, so kids will want to do it themselves. It can be even more effective, when a group of kids does it. This can help to bond playgroups of kids, and siblings.

30.   *Dyslexia*

The British Dyslexia Association says:[23]

> The BDA has adopted the Rose (2009) definition of dyslexia:
>
> Dyslexia is a learning difficulty that primarily affects the skills involved in accurate and fluent word reading and spelling. Characteristic features of dyslexia are difficulties in phonological awareness, verbal memory and verbal processing speed. Dyslexia occurs across the range of intellectual abilities. It is best thought of as a continuum, not a distinct category, and there are no clear cut-off points. Co-occurring difficulties may be seen in aspects of language, motor co-ordination, mental calculation, concentration and personal organisation, but these are not, by themselves, markers of dyslexia. A good indication of the severity and persistence of dyslexic difficulties can be gained by examining how the individual responds or has responded to well-founded intervention.
>
> In addition to these characteristics:
>
> The British Dyslexia Association (BDA) acknowledges the visual and auditory processing difficulties that some individuals with dyslexia can experience, and points out that dyslexic readers can show a combination of abilities and difficulties that affect the learning process. Some also have strengths in other areas, such as design, problem solving, creative skills, interactive skills and oral skills.

Matrixial Science explains these problems as arising from difficulties in connection between the thinking / feeling brain (where all that creativity happens) and the "computer" brain. We know from the *Matrixial Brain Experiments*, that we

---

[23] https://www.bdadyslexia.org.uk/dyslexia/about-dyslexia/what-is-dyslexia

can change how that connection works.

Here, we are looking at reading dyslexia, which is one of six different recognised types:[24]

Here are the three main types of dyslexia.

- **Primary dyslexia:** This is the most common type of dyslexia, and is a dysfunction of, rather than damage to, the left side of the brain (cerebral cortex) and does not change with age. There is variability in the severity of the disability for Individuals with this type of dyslexia, and most who receive an appropriate educational intervention will be academically successful throughout their lives. Unfortunately, there are others who continue to struggle significantly with reading, writing, and spelling throughout their adult lives. Primary dyslexia is passed in family lines through genes (hereditary) or through new genetic mutations and it is found more often in boys than in girls.
- **Secondary or developmental dyslexia:** This type of dyslexia is caused by problems with brain development during the early stages of fetal development. Developmental dyslexia diminishes as the child matures. It is also more common in boys.
- Trauma **dyslexia:** This type of dyslexia usually occurs after some form of brain trauma or injury to the area of the brain that controls reading and writing. It is rarely seen in today's school-age population.

Other types of learning disability include:

- The term **visual dyslexia** is sometimes used to refer to visual processing disorder, a condition in which the brain does not properly interpret visual signals.
- The term **auditory dyslexia** has been used to refer to auditory processing disorder. Similar to visual processing disorder, there are problems with the brain's processing of sounds and speech.
- **Dysgraphia** refers to the child's difficulty holding and controlling a pencil so that the correct markings can be made on the paper.

---

[24] https://www.medicinenet.com/dyslexia/article.htm

The same *Healing* works for children and adults. When working with kids under age 7, we need to use the "cushioning", which we explained in the *Child Lines* Chapter.

Scenario
The Client self-reports that they, or their child suffers from dyslexia.

Healing
Step 1
1.   Find a passage in a book.
2.   Try reading it out loud.

Step 2
1.   Feel a connection, in your head, with Second You: You2.
2.   This is just you: yourself, looking at you.
3.   You2 is just over your shoulder.
4.   Allow You2's head to connect with yours.

Step 3
1.   You2 can see your head.
2.   You2 can see you looking at the page.
3.   You2 can see the space between your eyes and the page.

Step 4
1.   Now: let You2 use your eyes.
2.   Direct your eyes to the page and the words.

3.   Just let You₂ tell you what the words say.

4.   Just speak what You₂ tells you each word says.

Step 5

1.   OK: relax.

2.   Let the You₂ connection drop.

End.

Explaining

We have been amazed at the effect of this *Healing*: instantly. Suddenly, the words come through loud and clear. It's like a different person is doing the reading. Both with adults and children.

The connections within the Architecture of the mind are now working as they should. It makes reading easy.

After Care

Making these connections work, without interference, takes practice. The Client wants to get to the point where the connections just link automatically. That will happen, as the needed patterns are created in the "computer" brain. As soon as the Client (or their child) experiences this "connected" reading, it gives a huge confidence boost. This enables the reader top stop trying to control their Anxiety. It's that attempt at control which is interfering with the *Anxiety-Soothing Rhythm*. That in turn creates confusion in the thinking/feeling brain, which interferes with the reading function.

The BDA does amazing work, especially with children. We don't want to discourage your child from using that help. This Recipe can just make that help even more successful.

31.   Autism

Ambitious About Autism says:[25]

What is autism?

Autism affects the way a person communicates and how they experience the world around them. It is considered a spectrum condition. While autistic people share some similar characteristics, they are also all different from each other. The autism spectrum isn't linear from high to low but varies, just as one person might vary from another.

Some people with autism are able to live relatively independent lives but others may face additional challenges, including learning disabilities, which means their support needs are different.

How does autism affect people?

Autism is a hidden or invisible disability. You can't see if someone is autistic just by looking at them and some people might not have been diagnosed when you meet them. There are some behaviours and ways of communication that an autistic person may use but these aren't universal as every autistic person is different.

The characteristics of autism vary from one person to another, but there are four main areas of difference.

Social interaction

Autistic people may find socialising and social interactions difficult. There are lots of unwritten rules that we use when talking to someone else, and these rules aren't always the same. Autistic people can find these

---

[25]   https://www.ambitiousaboutautism.org.uk/information-about-autism/ understanding-autism/what-is-autism

rules difficult to remember or confusing because they aren't always applied in the same way. This means autistic people often find it difficult to understand other people's intentions and express their own feelings.

Social interactions can often be tiring for autistic people and difficulties 'reading' other people can lead to loneliness and isolation. Autistic people don't lack the skills to interact with other people, they simply need more information and support to socialise with others.

Social imagination

Autistic people can find it harder to understand abstract concepts. For example, they can struggle to understand another person's point of view – or if they know it in theory, they may still struggle to imagine what it might be.

Differences in social imagination can make it harder for people with autism to cope with new, unfamiliar or unexpected situations. As a result many autistic people like to know what is going to happen in advance and have set routines for the activities they do. They can also have routines and repetition around things they like such as clothes, food, hobbies and conversations.

Many autistic people also have intense and highly focused *interests* from an early age. These interests and hobbies often provide them with lots of enjoyment and can be a huge source of joy.

Social communication

When you talk to another person, you listen to what they are saying, look at the actions they make with their face and body and think of what to say in response. Autistic people find it a lot harder to interpret both spoken language and body language, which can make communication more difficult. There are so many aspects of communication to take in at once, it can sometimes be too much for an autistic person to process all of this information and also respond.

Some autistic people have little or no speech or delayed language development – or they communicate in a different way - using pictures, sounds or gestures for example. This doesn't mean that they don't understand what is being said, often an autistic person can take in more information than they give out. This creates a disparity in what someone understands and what they communicate.

Autistic people can take instructions very literally and struggle to understand things like sarcasm or irony.

Sensory differences
Autistic people process sensory information differently and this can impact how they interact with the environment and their ability to interact with other people.
An autistic person can be 'under' or 'over' sensitive in any of the senses – including sight, hearing and balance. This means sounds, lights, touch and smells can be painful or very uncomfortable.

To reduce discomfort, some autistic people may wear sunglasses indoors or wear ear defenders – or prefer not to be touched or only eat specific foods.

We find that one of the core problems expressed in autism is that the sufferer has problems with processing their relationship with the outside world. There's the same amount of information (sights, sounds, smells, touches) coming in, as for everyone else. But the autism sufferer has problems in processing that information.

In *Secret Self*, Chapter 3, we explain the *Systems Architecture* by which we process that incoming information. We transform those signals into what we might call "chemical information". This passes through our brain system, which arranges itself under patterns created in our "computer" brain.

It's a complex process. When it is going wrong, we need to find out where in the journey of that information – coming in from the world – the problems are happening.

What does seem to be going on at the root of autism problems, is that the sufferer is allowing too much information in. This is what triggers what we observe as "shut down" and "shut out" behaviour.

We are born to see only a tiny part of the spectrum of light. Different animals see other parts of the spectrum. Imagine if your eye was malfunctioning, so that you were seeing like an eagle does: with 8 times better magnification, and a wider range of colour, including UV light. Just to open our eyes would, in our brain, feel like we were "tripping out". To try and walk just across the room, would be a nightmare journey. What would you do? Close your eyes, and shut out all that extra information from the world which is overwhelming your brain. You would be suffering Eagled-Autism.

So, we want to allow the "computer" brain to take more control over this information receiving process.

Scenario
A Client self-reports classic autism spectrum issues with themselves, or their child.

31A   Healing for Adults
Step 1
1.   Close your eyes.
2.   See yourself getting into your car.
3.   It can be the car you have.

4.   Or a dream car: G Wagon, Rolls-Royce: whatever.
5.   Sit comfortably behind the wheel. Adjust your seat.
6.   It may be day or night: that's up to you.

Step 2

1.   Look in your rear-view mirror.
2.   See yourself in a time of distress.
3.   Open your eyes.
4.   Blink a few times.

Step 3

1.   Close your eyes.
2.   You're back in your safe car.
3.   Look up at where the rear-view mirror is.

Step 4

1.   Feel a connection, in your head, with Second You: You$_2$.
2.   This is just you: yourself, looking at you.
3.   You$_2$ is sitting in the passenger seat.
4.   Allow You$_2$'s head to connect with yours.

Step 5

1.   You$_2$ can see your head.
2.   You$_2$ can see you looking at the rear-view mirror.
3.   You$_2$ can see the space between your eyes and the rear-view mirror.

4.   You$_2$ can see the distance between the rear-view
       mirror, and what you saw back there
       behind you.

Step 6

1.   Now: let You$_2$ use your eyes.
2.   Look in the rear-view mirror.
3.   Try to see yourself in distress.
4.   Keep trying.

Step 7

1.   Open your eyes.
2.   Blink and breathe.

Step 8

1.   Close your eyes.
2.   You're back in your safe car.
3.   Look up at where the rear-view mirror is.
4.   Feel a connection, in your head, with Second
       You: You$_2$.
5.   Now: let You$_2$ use your eyes.
6.   Look in the rear-view mirror.
7.   Try to see yourself in distress.
8.   Keep trying.

Step 9

1.   Open your eyes.
2.   Relax.

                    End.

Explaining

This is using *Psychotectics* to alter the connection between the "computer" brain and stimulus from the world. The "distressed you" is how your thoughts usually interpret your experiences in the world.

By connecting the "computer" brain, we dislocate these thoughts: the habits of interpreting experience. This allows ordinary experiences to happen, without interference from other layers of the experience interpretation process.

After Care

This isn't an instant fix. What can happen is that the Client sees an immediate change in how they experience reality. But this tends to be temporary. Yet, even that small window onto a life - where experience of the world can be felt differently - is gold dust. It's like allowing a blind person to see a chink of light.

The person's own natural-born systems then have a clue where to go looking for solutions, with new felt confidence that solutions can be found. Rather than "shutting out", it becomes a process of "looking in".

31B   Healing for Children

Step 1

1.   Let's keep our eyes open for now.
2.   Let's use two fingers of one hand to tap-tap our arm.

3.   Yaay!

Step 2

1.   Now, let's get Unicorn to sit by your shoulder.
2.   Give Unicorn a stroke with your hand.

Step 3

1.   OK. Now you can let Unicorn guide you.
2.   Let Unicorn hold your two fingers.
3.   Let Unicorn tell you when to tap.

Step 4

1.   Let Unicorn feel you breathing. In ...out.
2.   Yaay!
3.   Now, let Unicorn tap-tap your fingers, as you breathe.

Step 5

1.   Open your eyes.
2.   Relax.

End.

Explaining

This combines *Biomorphics* and *Psychotectics*, to give a very light-touch *Healing*. Yet, it can be very meaningful. Although we are getting the Child to use Unicorn, we are actually helping the child to take more control.

That control comes from the balance between what

they are sensing, and what they are thinking, with their breathing in the middle. Like the child is shaping their experience of the world to their natural rhythm.

Aural and music therapy for autistic children uses a similar insight.

After Care
This is a lovely little *Healing* exercise. It's not a cure. What is does provide is a way for the Child to take "time out" from a cycle of experiences that have become distressing.

This *Healing* can also be combined really usefully with the *Emotional Balance* Technique.

We are working on providing the child with reassuring, confidence-building pathways of autistic confusion. The child is only being fed each Recipe once: well, with enough repetitions for the child to "get it". After that, the child can take control of their own *Healing*. To re-learn the natural balance that is their birth right.

CHAPTER 10

RAINBOWS

Now, in this final Chapter, it's time for a bit of fun!

In Part 2, Section 6, we say:

In Congruence Interface Therapy (CIT), we use You₂ Avatar techniques, to engage <Constructs>. By which we kind of mean computer programs in your EM cloud:

- *CIT Morphonics*: we can use these as I0|W| interfaces, to change your interaction with the external world, as in improving your writing skills;
- *CIT Holonics*: we can use these to destabilise /S/ <coherence>, as in the *Memory Wipe*;
- we can use them in conjunction with Biomorphics, to effect medicinal interventions.

The capacity for CIT to create interfaces between the Self and the |W|orld is limited only, it seems, by our imagination.

We're going to look in this Chapter at three applications of *Matrixial Healing* Techniques. What we want to do here, is explain the Techniques, demonstrated by reference to particular areas of life activity. The reader can then have fun, trying out applications of the Techniques to different activities within these areas.

Just trying things out, and seeing what happens, is how many of the Recipes in this book have been developed. That's how all science works. We have a theory. We then think of practical applications to test the theory:

experimentation. Then we try to work out from success or failure, what that tells us about the theory.

So, don't be shy to try. In this book we've focused on around 30 broad categories of Recipe use for *Matrixial Healing* Techniques. There are many more uses out there waiting to be discovered.

32.   *Sporting Up*

All sports involve a physical and mental conversation between the Player, and the playing environment. That environment could be a gym bench, a rugby scrum, a ski slope.

We'd like to invite Players to try it and see. To get the idea of the Technique from the following Recipes, then have a go in their own sporting activity.

Gym Scenario

The Client would like to improve their ability to do circuits, body press, squat, lift weights.

32A   Healing for Gym

PART 1: BEFORE YOU START

Step 1

1.   You can sit down, or stand. Whatever works for you.

Step 2

1.   You can close your eyes, or keep them open.
2.   Take the palm of your writing hand.
3.   Place it over your tummy: just where your tummy button is.
4.   Make sure to leave a little gap between your palm and your tummy. This is really important. The gap should be a finger-width.
5.   You can close your eyes, or keep them open.
6.   Focus on breathing in through the palm of your hand.
7.   Feel yourself drawing in breaths, through the palm of your hand.
8.   You can breathe deep or shallow. Slow or fast. Whatever works.

Step 3

1.   Now, close your eyes.
2.   Feel a connection, in your head, with Second You: You$_2$.
3.   This is just you: yourself, looking at you.
4.   You$_2$ is the far side of the gym.
5.   Allow You$_2$'s head to connect with yours.

Step 4

1.   Now, move your hand palm.
2.   Place it over your chest.
3.   Make sure to leave a little gap between your palm and your chest. This is really important. The gap should be a finger-width.

4. Focus on breathing out through the palm of your hand.
5. Feel that connection, in your head, with Second You: You$_2$.
6. This is just you: yourself, looking at you.
7. Allow You$_2$'s head to connect with yours.

Step 5
1. Now: move You$_2$ from the far side of the gym, to next to your shoulder.
2. You will feel resistance.

Step 6
1. Move your palm back to your tummy.
2. Keep trying to move You$_2$ from the far side of the gym, to next to your shoulder.
3. Move your palm again to your chest.
4. Keep trying to move You$_2$ from the far side of the gym, to next to your shoulder.
5. Eventually, you'll feel You$_2$ standing next to your shoulder.

Step 7
1. Swap hands.
2. Place your other hand over your chest.
3. Try to move You$_2$ back to the far side of the gym.
4. Move your other hand palm again to your chest.
5. Finish moving You$_2$ back to the far side of the gym.

Step 8

1.   OK: relax
2.   Open your eyes.
3.   Breathe.

End.

PART 2: DURING TRAINING

Step 1

1.   Just before beginning each round of exertion.
2.   You can close your eyes, or keep them open.

Step 2

1.   Feel that connection, in your head, with Second You: You$_2$.
2.   This is just you: yourself, looking at you.
3.   Allow You$_2$'s head to connect with yours.
4.   Pull You$_2$ from the far side of gym to your shoulder.
5.   Push You$_2$ back again.

Now do your activity.

End.

Explaining

In Part 1, we are helping you to:

• connect with your "computer" brain
• use your body to "bypass" your thinking head, and tell your "computer" brain what it needs and when.

This is, in terms of Matrixial Science, a fairly inaccurate way of explaining what's going on. But it contains the gist of what you need to know.

With Part 2, the idea is that you can instantly call on this connection. That works just before you start the activity (say, lifts or squats). It also works with the breaths you take during the activity. That's why, at Part 1, we linked the You2 connection to different aspects of breathing. So that your breathing itself "pumps" the connection.

Golf Scenario
The Client would like to improve their ability to hit shots with regularity. This Healing will help with straightness. You'll find that you're hitting a model shot.

Obviously, try this all out on the practice range first: not in the middle of your monthly four ball medal match!

32B   Healing for Golf

PART 1: STANCE

Step 1
1.   Address the ball.
2.   Grip with your left hand,[26] and allow the club to rest behind the ball.

---

[26] for left-handed players, just reverse the hand labels

Step 2

1.   You can close your eyes, or keep them open.
2.   Feel a connection, in your head, with Second You: You$_2$.
3.   This is just you: yourself, looking at you.
4.   You$_2$ is on your right side.
5.   Allow You$_2$'s head to connect with yours.
6.   Allow You$_2$'s head to connect with your left hand.
7.   You'll automatically feel yourself shifting hand position relative to the ball.

Step 3

1.   Now, grip with your right hand.
2.   You can close your eyes, or keep them open.
3.   Feel a connection, in your head, with Second You: You$_2$.
4.   This is just you: yourself, looking at you.
5.   You$_2$ is on your left side.
6.   Allow You$_2$'s head to connect with yours.
7.   Allow You$_2$'s head to connect with your right hand.
8.   You'll automatically feel yourself shifting hand position relative to the ball.

Step 4

1.   Now, you're feeling a balanced connection with You$_2$.
2.   It's like You$_2$ is spread across your field of awareness.

3.   Allow You2 to connect with your hips, legs and
      feet.

Step 5
1.   Under You2's guidance, you can feel your
      position changing, relative to the ball.
2.   Just go with it.

PART 2: ALIGNMENT
Step 1
1.   Look at the flag.
2.   Keeping your head's connection with You2,
      draw a visual line: from the flag to between your
      toes and the ball:

Step 2
1.   Keeping the You2 connection, extend that line
      behind you.
2.   Allow You2 to do a virtual swing of the club: it
      goes wherever it goes behind you, and comes
      back down that line.[27]

---

[27] you don't have to worry about the backswing mechanics: your starting
foot position, and posture, will do that work

PART 3: SWING

Step 1

1.   Now make whatever adjustments you want to make, with grip and shoulder and knee-bend position.

Step 2

1.   Feel that connection, in your head, with Second You: You$_2$.

2.   Close your eyes.

3.   Allow You$_2$ to make a virtual swing.

Step 3

1.   Open your eyes

2.   Breathe.

3.   Allow the You$_2$ connection to be there, but now just focus on your hands, being connected by You$_2$, with the ball.

Now swing!

                              End.

Explaining

This Technique works, even for complete beginners.

It takes a bit of practice, to integrate the You$_2$ connections into your swing set up. But, once you have the knack, it becomes automatic. It's a bit like You$_2$ is acting like one of those swing trainers:

https://planeswing.com/

The difference is that they are one-size-fits-all, and so don't fit you. Your own "computer" brain, by contrast, is fitting your swing action perfectly to you. You'll actually be able to feel - even on starting the backswing – whether it's going to be a good shot. You get used to the feeling of "letting go" into the You2 swing arc.

We've seen both beginner and experienced amateur golfers go "wow" after the first 3 to 5 shots. They see the ball flying dead straight, and with a perfect trajectory.

After Care
Using You2 in this way overcomes the basic bugbear of all golfers: regularity. Everything about you, physiologically and mentally, changes all the time. You're not the same person as the one who hit that last golf shot.

But your "computer" brain holds a swing pattern. In effect, it "tells" your body how to move. The body that you have in that moment. It's not that your swing stays constant: it's the *relationship* between you and your swing.

See you *Matrixial Golfers* at the next Open Championship!

33.   Sexing Up

Sex is all in the head, as the saying goes. Well, sex is definitely all in the head's relationship with the body: under stimulus.

Just as *Matrixial Healing* Techniques can soothe pain, they can create and enhance pleasure.

Scenario

The Client would like to discover more ways of having sexual experience, without actually having physical sex.

These Techniques needs two people. We'll call them *Giver* and *Receiver*.

33A   Virtuality Healing

Step 1

1.   Best both sitting or lying down for this.
        Receiver
2.   Take the top 2 fingers of your writing hand.
3.   OK, move them gently and slowly up and down your other arm: from elbow to wrist.

Step 2

1. Think of the feelings you get when you're starting to have sex.
2. And the place in your body you most feel those feelings.
3. Now, find with your fingers that place on your arm: which best connects – with those feelings and that place.
4. Just hold your fingers there.
5. Allow Giver to see that place on your arm.
6. Now, close your eyes.

Giver

Step 3

1. Place Giver's 2 fingers on that spot on Receiver's arm.
2. Start slowly pressing the 2 fingers up and down, and sideways: gently massaging that spot.

Step 4

1. Remind Receiver: "You can feel the connection with that special place and those perfect feelings."
2. Keep finger massaging.

Step 5

1. Tell Receiver: "Your thoughts can go wherever they want to go – inside or outside."
2. Keep finger massaging.

Step 6

1.   Tell Receiver: "I can feel your breathing
        changing, as your perfect feelings make contact
        with that perfect place."
2.   Keep finger massaging.

Step 7

1.   Repeat Steps 4-6, with word variations if you
        like.
2.   Keep finger massaging.

Step 8

1.   Receiver will let Giver know when to stop.

Step 9

1.   OK: relax
2.   Open your eyes.
3.   Breathe.

End.

Explaining

Technically, this is a combination of *Biomorphics* and
Psychotectics.

We're copying the nerve pathways by which the sensual
body and the brain usually connect with each other. Then,
we're linking them to a different stimulus point (the 2
fingers on the arm).

We could call this "virtual sex". It's very like what we do with ourselves to Pornhub.

After Care

This isn't a suggestion for replacing actual sex. Although, for a person who can't have physical sex right now (that time of the month, or soreness, or disability), it's a nice holiday from abstinence.

For those who are able to enjoy physical sex, this is an amazing warm up!

33B   Breathing Healing

Step 1

1.   Giver and Receiver are having actual sex.
2.   Giver (M) is behind Receiver (M or F).

Step 2

Giver

1.   Take the palm of your writing hand.
2.   Place it over Receiver's tummy: just where their tummy button is.
3.   Make sure to leave a little gap between your palm and their tummy. This is really important. The gap should be a finger-width.
4.   You can close your eyes, or keep them open.

Step 3

1.   Move your hand palm with Receiver, as they move.

2.   Maintain the gap.
3.   You'll feel Receiver "breathing in" though your palm.
4.   You'll feel your palm getting warm.
5.   You'll feel an increasingly intense connection with Receiver.

End.

Explaining

You'll know when to stop this one, because your Receiver will explode!

What's happening is that your palm is creating a (harmless) *Biomorphic* feedback in your Receiver. You don't say anything, and you don't need to. It happens automatically. That feedback intensifies the nerve stimulation in that area. It amplifies the sexual stimulation feelings of the Receiver.

After Care

Your partner can do the same for you.

Lie on your back. Allow your partner to take you in their hand. Your partner then places their open palm over your tummy. Enjoy the ride!

34.   Enjoying Energy

Feelings of connection are special. They don't rely upon us thinking something. Instead, these connections can alter our thinking. We all want to feel connected, to feel part of something.

We can start by feeling profound connection with ourselves. Then, we can extend connection to the world around us.

Scenario

The Client is unfamiliar with their own energy connections.

Healing

PART 1

Step 1

1.   Sit down for this.

2.   You can keep your eyes open.

Step 2

1.   Take the palm of your writing hand.

2.   Move it over your thigh.

3.   About a hand's breadth above your thigh.

4.   Now, close your eyes.

5.   Feel whatever you feel.

Step 3

1.   Now, move that hand over your tummy.

2.   About a hand's breadth away from your clothes.

3.   Feel whatever you feel.

Step 4

1.   Now, move that hand over your chest.

2.   About a hand's breadth away from your clothes.

3.   Feel whatever you feel.

Step 5

1.   Now, move that hand back over your tummy.

2.   About a hand's breadth away from your clothes.

3.   Feel the difference you feel.

Step 6

1.   Now, move that hand back over your thigh.

2.   About a hand's breadth away from your clothes.

3.   Feel the difference you feel.

Step 7

1.   Take your hand away.

2.   Open your eyes.

3.   Relax.

PART 2

Step 1

1.   Sit or stand for this.

2.   You can keep your eyes open.

3.   This only works with living things.

Step 2

1.   Take the palm of your writing hand.
2.   Now, hold it out to a bunch of flowers; or to
        flowers in a garden.
3.   You'll feel that tingling energy.

End.

Explaining

This is pure Biomorphics. The connections between the physical energies which the cells of all living things create. This isn't spooky "New Age" stuff.[28] That physical energy is as scientifically established as the electricity that comes out of a plug point.

You can see the electromagnetic energy with equipment which is standard in neuroscience labs. What the existence of this energy means, for being human, and connections between our Self and our world: well that's where the big theory books come in.

After Care

Try it with different types of flowers. You'll see that different flowers have different energy signatures. If you have a pet (dog or cat), try it with the pet. You can try it out with anything that's alive.

---

[28] we're not saying there's anything wrong with any of that: just drawing a distinction

There's a library full of *Matrixial Science* behind all this. How far the reader wishes to turn those pages is up to them: you're the boss of you. What we hope you can take away from the final words of this book, is one big idea. That you don't need to understand the science, to enjoy the benefits.

Just think of the problem, and apply the Steps in the relevant Recipe. *Matrixial Healing* works for you, instantly, and over time, because the Therapy Techniques help you to do one thing: to realise the power of You.

PART (2)
HEALING HOW

CHAPTER 11

MATRIXIAL SCIENCE

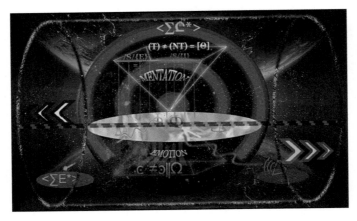

This graphic summarises how the Self fits together, in the world around each Self. Our explanations of all this make up *Matrixial Science*.

Matrixial Science is made up of 3 parts:
- the Theories about how all this works
- the Logic that unifies the theories
- the Experiments that provide real world evidence the predictions made by the Theories are valid. This "validates" the Theories.

The logic and science part of the Matrixial Project, involve new ways of understanding:

how we think about what we think

Matrixial Therapy is the application of that Science, to human problems. This Therapy uses *Matrixial Healing* Techniques: the equivalent of understanding how to use an x-ray machine, how to fit a plaster cast. The Techniques are practical applications of Therapy ideas.

The Recipes in this book are step-by-step guides for using the Techniques to remedy particular problems.

Helicopter View
We all find it useful to get a helicopter view. To rise up, out of all the detail. To get free from technicalities and complicated ideas. To see the landscape spread out below us.

The problem is: we are forever stuck, in our own helicopter. Permanently moored to the ground. When we try to leave the ground and gain height, all we are really doing is imagining. That imagination is just spreading our view around us at ground level.

We can't ever actually achieve that helicopter view of our Selfs. We can only engage in fantasies about it. There's nothing at all wrong with that. It's the way each of us, as Self, is born and made. But we can go badly wrong, if we decide to believe that what we just imagine is the landscape of reality.

When we leave aside the complicated ideas and vocabulary of *Matrixial Science*, this is the basic insight that remains. We can't escape from the confines of our own Selfs: but we don't need to, in order to understand our Selfs.

That understanding – the *Matrixial Self* – explains why and how we each see our Selfs and the world our Selfs live in. There's an architecture. That architecture is what makes that seeing possible, and what places limits on how and what we can see.

Just like the human body. There are billions of individual variations. But each of us has the body and genes that we have. There's no other way to be. Sure, there's prosthetics and gene therapy. There's a fascinating philosophical debate, going back to Aristotle, about how much something needs to change to become something else. Yet, our common understanding is the *Robocop* idea: we remain the same Self, even when only some parts of the organic body remain.

Matrixial Theory is not about understanding You, as a person. With all your individual and constantly changing life experiences. It's about understanding your *Architecture*. The architecture which we all share.

What the core *Matrixial Experiments* prove, is that the architecture is there, and more importantly, that you can't escape from it. We've all seen those optical illusion tests where scientists, having worked out how the eye system operates, can trick it. There's an architecture to the visual operating system. You can't escape the limits of the architecture.

In *Matrixial Therapy*, we are using our understanding of that architecture to reset your operating system. That's just what the Recipes do. Where you're within the range of architectural normality, the systems just work. If you're a psychopath, then you genuinely do have processes going on inside the architecture, which put you outside the range of the Recipes. So, any of you guys : well done for getting this far.

So, that's why we don't need to investigate your personality and life experiences. Your architecture works the same as everyone else. Its wiring suffers the same "short circuits" as billions of others. In the same way, a medical practitioner does not worry about what your personality type is, when diagnosing and mending your broken leg. It's a systems failure, and it's the same diagnosis and treatment for everyone.

Your helicopter can't fly. It wasn't created to do that. You can imagine it in flight as intensely as you like. That remains a feat of the imagination, not reality. Yet that imagination is your reality. That's all there is.

So, the mission of *Matrixial Therapy* is to repair the operating systems of that helicopter architecture. Then you can enjoy – without systems interference - your reality of thinking that you're feeling the experience of flying. This is what brings you balance, peace and power.

Matrixial Logic
Matrixial Logic is a toolkit. Unlike classical logic, it's a method for invention of new ideas.

Chapter 3 of *Matrixial Logic* set out a critique of classical logic, beginning with the *law of identity* proposition:

$$A=A$$

Matrixial Logic ("ML") begins with the *law of inequality* proposition:

$$A \neq A$$

As we write the foundational equations of ML:

$$(A) \neq (^{NOT}A) = [E]$$
$$\text{and}$$
$$(A) \neq (-A) = [I]$$

In ML, we take as our starting point the difference between anything and any other thing: even an iteration of the first thing.

We point out that reality – the world out there – is not a collection of identities at all. That the world is a universe of differences is the bedrock of the material sciences. Ever since modern science was invented in the 17th century.

The idea that all things have an immanent essence – an identity - is wholly unscientific. It was a prejudice amongst the classical Greek thinkers. That prejudice became transmuted, through a curious admixture of Platonic philosophy, Aristotelian physics and Middle Eastern esoteric deism, into what became orthodox Christianity.

At the dawn of the modern scientific era, logic attempted to rescue thinking from the dogmas of medieval scholasticism. This paralleled and paved the way for the Copernican and Newtonian revolutions.

But, as material science went on to engage with the universe, logic remained stuck in the ruts originally made by ox carts trundling past the groves of classic Greek academies.

We say that ML is actually the logic of the material sciences. Not just our method of thinking about the world, but the way that the universe actually is.

The Matrixial Self

The human Self is part of that reality. It's the most difficult part to see: each of us trying to gaze into our goldfish bowl of Self: from the outside – where we can never be.

We restate a core proposition of *Secret Self*:

Mentation

How we can think governs what we can think

Emotion

What we can emote governs how we emote

Just as the material universe acts in accordance with laws discovered over the last 400 years, so the Self is governed by its place in objective reality.

Our subjective self /S/: is bounded by a Systems Architecture (we'll explain this more below):

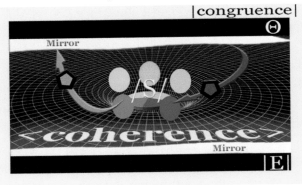

By understanding, with ML, the processes of that Systems Architecture of Self, we are able to derive laws of Matrixial Science.

The Matrixial Brain

The last 2 decades of neuroscience investigation have enabled a paradigm shift in our understanding the human brain. We are no longer limited to the attempt to understand subjectivity and personality, by reference to the mechanical interactions of synapses via chemicals and ionic electrical transmissions.

We now have empirical evidence for interaction between electromagnetic fields in the brain (arising from synaptic activity) and synaptic transmission timing.[29]

We, as Selfs, are complexes of these interactions of energy fields. Not "energy" in the spooky New Age sense. But energy just like the stuff which powers your phone and computer.

It's simplistic but contextually useful, to say that ML equations are *field equations*. Not quantitatively (they are not equations of numbers): but the qualitative logic of field equations.

The equations represent how we actually think: about everything. The equations allow us to "see inside" the logic of how we think.

This is the basic Table of equations. It obviously doesn't mean much without the explanations: to be found in *Matrixial Logic* and *Secret Self*.

---

[29] as is presently thought. Which is really just a prejudice. The door is now open to investigation of how EM fields are generated by cellular activity throughout the body.

Fundamental Equations

Form in [E]	$(A) \neq (nA) = [E]$
Form in [I]	$(A) \neq (-A) = [I]$
<Node> in [E]	$\Box[E]^n \neq \Box[E]^n \sum <E>$
<Node> in [I]	$\Delta[I]^n \neq \Delta[I]^n \sum <I>$

Modes of Interaction

|W|orld <Node>	$\|W\| \sum <I> => \|EF\|$
|P| <Node>	$\|P\| \sum <I> => \|EF\|$
/S/ <Node>	$/S/ \sum <I> => \|EF\|$

Exclusion Function: Quantised

Capacity Gapping	$(\geq\varsigma) \neq (\leq\Theta) \int[x]$
Plurality	$\Delta\int[x]^n => (\epsilon) \mid \Delta\int[x]^n => (\ni)$

Ohm Function: Qualitised

Aggregation	$(\epsilon) \neq (\ni) \sum \Omega^n$
<Affect>	$(\epsilon) \neq (n\epsilon) = [\text{€}]$
Referral to /S/	$[\Box \, \text{€}^1] \neq [\Box \, \text{€}^n] \sum <\text{€}>$

<Thought>

Potential	$\Delta<T^n> \mid \infty$
VCIP	$\sum <\text{€}> (T) \neq (-T) = \text{ŧ}[I]$

Theta Axis

<Constructs>	$(T) \neq (nT) = \Theta$
[T] Synchronisation	$\underline{\Theta^n = \|IO\| = \|W\|}$

$$\sum \|\text{₡}\|$$

CHAPTER 12

SCIENCE AND PRACTICE

A good scientist may not make for the best practitioner: and indeed the other way round.

You don't have to understand the Fundamental Equations, and the complex interplay of scientific theory that they describe, in order to use *Matrixial Healing* techniques. Indeed, part of the power of *Matrixial Science* is that it leads to therapies which are simple Step-based. You can just follow the Steps and out pops the *Healing* result.

Matrixial Science has this in common with much else in science. You don't need a degree in quantum physics to do car repairs. You do need a medical degree to treat the complexities of human physical ailments. What *Matrixial Science* allows is a realisation of transparency. Making clear what appears to be complexity in the organising System of the Self.

This is why, in *Matrixial Therapy*, we don't need to spend countless hours making a Client go over and over things which are bothering them. Any more than your doctor makes you repeat that you have a broken leg: that is the diagnosis transparency that modern medical science brings.

Matrixial Therapy starts from the position that, whatever is the problem, it's a problem with process. A problem with the way that the Client is trying to organise their mind and its relationship with their body.

There is a definitely a right way: the one that we were all born with. The mechanics of that grow, change and adapt through life. The essential Systems Architecture stays the same.

The task of *Matrixial Therapy* is simply to help the Client to reconnect the relationships within their Self, to the Systems Architecture that makes the Self work.

What makes a good *Matrixial Healing* practitioner? Whatever works. It's made much easier by the fact the Practitioner is not having to interpret what the Client is saying.

It's a core value of *Matrixial Healing* that we take the Client at face-value. You'll see in the Recipes Section that each Recipe begins with "and this is what the Client self-reports…"

After all, the only expert on You, is You. This is not about you, as a Client, diagnosing what is wrong with you: but reporting how you consider your life experience is going less right than you'd like it. Well: you're the one that knows. It's your life.

So, *Matrixial Therapy* is not about challenging the Client's thinking. That's the path of psychotherapy, and particularly Cognitive Behavioural Therapy. We view these as dealing with the subjective mind. *Matrixial Healing* is about gaining |congruence| between the subjective and the objective mind.

You'll read this distinction a lot in the *Explaining* parts of the recipes. These, of course, are more for the Practitioner than the Client.

It took the whole book of *Secret Self* adequately to explain this distinction - and even that was a summary.

For Practitioner purposes, let's set it out like this, with reference to the graphic:

To explain further, let's also refer to this graphic:

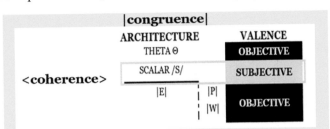

The bottom part of the second graphic:

is pretty familiar territory in common knowledge.

We all know that there's a |W|orld out there. Most of us who aren't professional philosophers of a certain type (called Dualists) are pretty OK with the idea that: the world out there is real and we can understand it through science.

There might be a God, or more than one out there too. But we tend not to let that concern us when we have a broken leg, or want to use mobile phone technology.

That takes us to |P|hysiology: basically, the body. Most of us are fine with the idea that the body is kind of like a machine. It works in definite ways, it can break down, and it can get broken. Some of us may not like the machine idea and just prefer to think of us having bodies and biological systems, just like other animals. They, too, can suffer injury and illness. And we have medical (veterinary) science, which can help to heal these breakdowns.

The body and the things out there in the universe: that's the *objective world*. Not many people (outside of some philosophy rooms and quantum physics labs) have an issue with that view of things.

Then there's our |E|motions. This is where *Matrixial Science* starts down a different pathway. Not just us. There's a whole load of brain scientists who promote a theory called *Interoception*. Whilst we part company with them later down the path, we are all in agreement that what we think of as "emotions" are part of the objective world.

In common sense, we think of our |E|motions as being definitely subjective. Completely personal and individual. Well, they are in the same sense that everyone's heart, lungs and kidney functions in a definite individual way. It's your DNA fingerprint, and nobody else's. But we are fine to accept that there are *systems in how* everyone's heart, lungs and kidney functions: and these *systems* are the same for everyone. If they weren't then medical science just wouldn't work.

So, without a book-length explanation of why, *Matrixial Science* says that our | E | motions work under a common system, which is also part of the *objective world*.

Now, we're going to leap up a layer:

ARCHITECTURE	VALENCE
THETA Θ	**OBJECTIVE**

Matrixial Science says that our brain creates two different sorts of mind: the /S/ubjective mind (which is thoughts and feelings – a different sort of thoughts); and the Objective mind (which we call Theta – symbol Θ).

Brain science, over the last 20 years, has shown us that there are actually different physical parts to the brain: to what's going on inside our heads. There's the grey matter stuff, with chemical and electrical signals whizzing around. There's also a "cloud" of electromagnetic ("EM") connections. The grey matter produces electrical energy, which fizzes in the EM cloud. The EM cloud gets the grey matter to send signals at certain times.

Secret Self shows how all this fits together. Together with *Matrixial Logic*, this is the science which shows how the /S/ layer is limited in the way it works. The science shows how the Theta Θ EM cloud works, in co-ordination with the grey matter.

This is the key point: the Theta Θ EM cloud is also part

of the *objective world*. It is actually connected through I T I ime with that external I W I orld. We use that strange notation I T I ime, in matrixial writing, because it reflects the way that "time" really works.

I T I ime is not a flow, like a river. It's a sequence of gaps: more like stepping stones over a river. Those gaps are tiny parts of a second. They are what actually make up the reality in and around us.

Then we come to this layer of the graphic:

what we call the /S/subjective (technically "Scalar") layer. This is what we commonly think of as being our "mind". The thoughts, feelings, ideas, judgments, values and so on. Everything that makes me a <Me>.

We call this a *continuum of infinity*. By which we mean that the layer stretches out forever, in all directions. That is the human mind, as we recognise it. But that's not all there is to the human mind. That *subjective* mind is sandwiched as a layer between the *objective mind*, the *objective world*.

Matrixial Science is the only discipline that looks at the Self quite like this.

Then, back to this graphic:

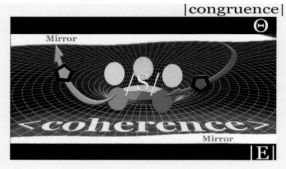

we say that the *subjective* mind:

- works by equivalence: by comparing thoughts with each other
- is always trying to find <coherence>: that is, the sense that thought A is equivalent to some other thought.

Equivalence does not mean "equals" or "identical to". You don't think that one apple is identical to another apple. But you may be perfectly happy to treat one apple as being the same as if it were the other apple. That's *equivalence*.

So we, seek <coherence> in our /S/subjective thoughts. It's just how we, as human beings, are made.

We are born with some help in that, because there's this gravitational attraction amongst parts of our thinking and feeling. We call these the 5 Slices of our Personality: Needs and Wants; Chemistry; Empathy; Challenge; and Security. These are the 5 coloured "planets" in the graphic. The relationship between them - which changes all the time – is what gives shape to our recognisable personality.

These thoughts and feelings, we call {idents}. That's the grey and purple arrows in the graphic. These "bounce off" the Mirrors. These Mirrors are at the boundary between the *subjective* layer of the mind, and the *objective* layers.

Finally, we have surrounding the graphic the label: |congruence|. This is really what *Matrixial Therapy* is all about: gaining |congruence| between the subjective and the objective mind. By which we mean: helping the connections to work between these layers of the Self.

Now, if this was just theory, the reader would be justified in saying: so what? The thing is, Experiments have provided strong evidence for the theory. We don't like to say "prove", as that raises all sorts of theoretical questions. Let's just say, if an umbrella keeps the rain off you, that's strong evidence the umbrella is water-resistant.

You can read the detail of these tests in the *Matrixial Brain: Experiments in Reality*. The Experiments show that the theories of *Matrixial Science* are dealing with matters of reality. As the Matrixial saying goes: *whatever's going on here: something's going on.*

In the middle of all this are biological processes, which allow it all to have life. The key process is what we call the *Anxiety-Soothing Rhythm* ("ASR"). The ASR is vital to so much that we create and practice in *Matrixial Therapy*.

The ASR describes a process which is perfect. We are born with it. The *Anxiety* is how our baby body communicates with our baby brain. The *Anxiety* gets a baby to act out, to cry and wriggle and so on. In search of getting what the baby needs. A carer supplies what the baby needs. This triggers the *Soothing* response. That *Soothing* is always equal in intensity to the *Anxiety*.

We learn, through the ASR, how to adjust our behaviour and thoughts. This carries on throughout our lives. As our subjective mind becomes more complex, we find endless ingenious ways of *interfering* with the ASR. An important element of *Matrixial Therapy*, is to find ways of helping ourselves to stop or limit that interference.

This is why we are able to provide *Healing* techniques that are not about changing You. There is therapy that is all about telling you there's a better You: over there on a high mountain top. If you just challenge yourself into changes, then eventually, you might get there. And most people give up.

Matrixial Healing knows there is perfection in you

already. You were born with it. Born with a perfect ASR. *Matrixial Science* shows how the ASR fits into the *Systems Architecture* of the Self.

Together, these allow the creation of the Recipes of *Matrixial Healing*. A Practitioner should know the basics of Matrixial Science: what's written in this Part, and what come out of the *Explaining* paragraphs for each *Healing*.

As a Practitioner, it's about knowing the Recipes. Listening to what the Client says about themselves. Accepting their truth of what the Client self-reports. Then applying the Recipe Steps. Relieving the Client of their pain and problems: without making them have to re-experience them. Not giving the Client hope: but results.

Matrixial Healing is about helping the Client to find their own balance, peace and power. It's all there already. It just needs the Steps to make the connections.

CHAPTER 13

BASIC BIOMORPHICS

Biomorphics is a branch of Matrixial Science.

Technical Explanation
In Secret Self, Chapter 9, we provided a technical explanation:

Biomorphics provides therapeutic interventions to restore Biomorphic Autonomic Balance ("BAB"):

- by stimulating the ASR.
- by displacing /S/ interference in the ASR.
- by reducing the interference energy input available to /S/ so as to produce and maintain Shadow Slices.

The core of Biomorphics is understanding that:

(1) We are born with a perfectly functioning ASR, which creates and maintains BAB.

(2) The ASR is common to complex sentient life.

(3) In humans, the Vagal Nerve is central to ASR operation.

(4) What differentiates humans is the existence of the /S/ continuum, and the complexity of its neurological system.

(5) This complexity grants power to /S/ to interfere in the ASR in a way not available to other complex sentient life.

(6)   It's through interface between /S/ and the ASR
        that we learn in /S/ubjectivity, and that
        we develop a <Me> personality.

(7)   That which is <Me>, moment to moment, is
        constrained by the limits of BAB.

(8)   When we try to subvert, alter, or push beyond
        BAB, we induce trauma in the Self.

(9)   We absolutely cannot think ourselves better. We
        cannot improve on the ASR perfection endowed
        in us by nature.

(10)   Encouraging us to use /S/{identation} to inter
        fere more in the ASR is irrational.

(11)   Therapy which seeks to use {idents} within
        the /S/ continuum to heal, challenge, or change
        other {idents}, by reference to
        external objectivised Mimetics,
        has either zero, placebo, or harmful effects.

(12)   Biomorphic techniques are explicitly directed at
        restoration of BAB.

Empirical observation (experiment) has demonstrated that simple hand and breath movements have immediate effect:

- to restore BAB
- to minimise /S/ interference.

We have also discovered that 3-5 repetitions of a Biomorphic Exercise, are sufficient to engage | congruence |, such that Θ<Constructs> can be accessed by volitional /S/{idents}.

349

The result is that you can achieve some of the effect in ASR on BAB simply by recapitulating in your |M|entation, the Biomorphic Exercise.

Plain English Explanation

Biomorphics deals with how the *Anxiety-Soothing Rhythm* ("ASR") works inside us, within the "sandwich" layers of the Self.

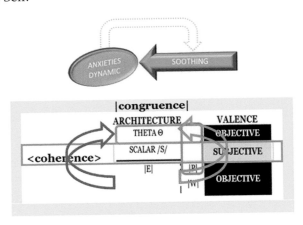

The ASR promotes Biomorphic Autonomic Balance ("BAB"). Now, this BAB is not a place. It's a process. It's like a top that keeps spinning, unless something gets in the way.

The BAB is extremely powerful. We could poetically call it our "life force". It's the system which we are all born with, to regulate our ability to live.

The BAB is the dynamic element of the objective parts of

ourselves. That's what the green and orange arrows mean in the graphic. The BAB links our body and the EM cloud part of our brain.

You can see the BAB at work in animals like dogs, cats, chimps. All the animals that have a similar set-up to us, as a body linked with a brain that works objectively. You can see the Anxiety-Soothing Rhythm working in those animals. That's how we train them: by working with their natural Anxiety and giving them rewards.

But those animals don't have a massive great subjective mind, there as a middle layer. Whether they have a subjective layer at all is a debate for other days. What we know for sure, is that we definitely do.

What interferes with the BAB cycles is: us. Our subjective minds. Our thoughts and feelings are always tinkering with the BAB. We can't help it. And it's not like that's a bad thing. It's part of how we learn and grow.

But we are expert amateurs at this interference. We each know ourselves in ways that nobody else does: that's our expertise. But we are engaged in a lifelong pursuit of trial and error – of tinkering – in this BAB interference.

Biomorphic Healing is all about restoring BAB. To achieve that, we have to get that subjective tinkering out of the way, for a short while. We do this by creating <coherence>

in /S/. This is like "freezing" the movement of our mind. Only for a few seconds. That's all it takes.

In those moments, the BAB is able to restore its balance: to start "spinning" freely again. This, in turn, adjusts the working of our subjective mind.

In Biomorphic techniques like *Angel Wings* (which we'll meet later) you get that sense of the dancefloor of your head, crowded with thoughts: emptying. This is <coherence> in /S/.

We achieve this <coherence> by getting you to allow your ASR to work, without interference from your thoughts. Biomorphic *Angel Wings* get you to feel the power of your BAB, by releasing your ASR from interference.

Having restored BAB for a few moments, you feel different: in a good way. You're more than free again to go think whatever thoughts you want to think. But suddenly, you are thinking those thoughts in a Self that feels balance, peace and power.

So then you want to think thoughts that reflect balance, peace and power. Instead of thoughts that are (for you) unbalanced, unpeaceful and disempowering.

CHAPTER 14

PRIMARY PSYCHOTECTICS

Psychotectics is another branch of Matrixial Science.

Technical Explanation
In Secret Self, Chapter 9, we provided a technical explanation:

Psychotectics is the science that sets out empirically observed principles of how the /S/{idents} continuum operates in infinity, under its |congruence| boundary conditions.

Psychotectics then provides therapeutic interventions:
- like ADT, which use {identation} to effect restoration of Autonomic Dynamic Balance.
- like Congruence Interface Therapy, which you saw in the *I-Pen*, Memory *Wipe*, and Dream *Running Experiences*.

The core of Psychotectics is understanding that:

(13)   All {idents} are fictional: they have no objective existence, but are absolutely real for the Self.

(14)   The Self seeks <coherence> in {identation}.

(15)   That seeking is innately imposed by the boundary conditions of /S/ubjectivity: the reality that the infinite continuum of /S/ is bounded by objective reality in |E| and Θ.

(16)   Those boundaries cannot be seen from the outside, within the Self.

(17)   Those boundaries exist for the Self only as Mirrors within /S/.

(18)   We use those Mirrors to orient <coherence>.

(19)   We reflect "torchlight" {idents} from those Mirrors, then apply other {idents} to the reflections.

(20)   This Mirroring process is fundamental to our sense of <Me> identity: of MySelf.

(21)   The Slices are anchored in the ASR. It is how the ASR manifests in our <coherence>.

(22)   The Slices dynamic acts like gravity in our /S/ continuum. It shapes the "torchlight" we shine inside ourselves, and reflect off boundary Mirrors.

The Slices are not visible to {idents}. They are not things that exist. They are a way of thinking and talking about how the ASR generates an automatic "base level" <coherence> in /S/.

This base-level reset is what we mean by Autonomic Dynamic Balance.

Plain English Explanation
Going back to this graphic:

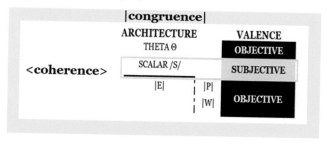

Psychotectics is about dealing with the "top layer": what's technically termed Theta Θ. Physically, this "top layer" can be looked as being part of the way the EM cloud works.

We use the *You₂ Avatar* as a way of getting the Client to connect with the EM cloud. It's a way of saying: rather than your subjective mind whizzing round, creating sparks for the EM cloud, allow your EM cloud to direct the sparks creation.

When you connect with the EM cloud, you can definitely feel it. We use suggestion about You₂ being some distance away from you, or sometimes closer to you. These are just ways of helping you to establish the connection.

Using the *You₂ Avatar*, we are allowing |congruence| to wrap around your subjective mind. Or, to think of it another (but less realistic way), look at the Objective / Subjective / Objective layers in the graphic like building blocks. We are moving the pink block sideways to create a gap. Or, we can think of it as making the pink block thinner, or more transparent.

Another way of thinking about Theta Θ, is as a kind of computer program. It takes whatever thoughts and feelings are going on in your subjective mind, and makes them into Yes/No equations.

So, with the *You2 Avatar*, we are getting these computer programs to run the Self. Just for a few moments. That changes the landscape:

The Autonomic Dynamic Balance - the orange colour – allows the subjective mind to rearrange itself.

The BAB is what we might call the "bottom up" version, and the ADB the "top down" version.

Matrixial Healing therapies might use Biomorphics, or Psychotectics, or a combination of both. It depends on the problem. They both work to restore balance.

CHAPTER 15

TIME SCIENCE THERAPY

Matrixial Time

Each of us is like a spinning top. Going back to the graphic at the start of this Chapter:

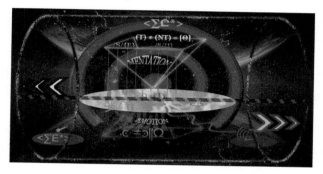

The top half - thinking - "spins" backwards in time: the white arrows. The bottom half – feelings – spins forward in time: the red arrows. The important thing is: that top needs to keep spinning:

Credit: Boden/Ledingham / Radius Images
Copyright: © Boden/Ledingham / Radius Images

357

A top is something that spins. That's how a top is what it is. In the same way, our "upper" and "lower" halfs spin. That is how we keep a balance.

The top is spinning on a surface, like a table. We spin in time. What Matrixial Science labels as |T|ime. This isn't time like the tick-tocks of a clock. It's not time like an arrow. It's not even the time that pops out of Einstein's relativity theories.

It's the |T|ime we experience, as Selfs, in the |W|orld. But, when we get to this point in explaining, simplicity necessarily begins to melt away.

As we say in Matrixial Science, each of us is a Being in Becoming. By that, we express the temporally dimensional character of human existence in a universe of reality. We say that: *it is temporal dimensionality that unifies these discreet beings as becomings.*

In doing so, we take seriously our propositions and empirical investigations into the quantum character of |T|ime. This allows us to identify the locus of |congruence| within each Self and between each Self and that which is (^{NOT}Self) as *temporal synchronisation*.

It helps if you think of this computer as running a clock, and that clock matches with the clock of the real world out there. In fact, there's an infinity of these clocks. One easy way of visualising that is to look at your smartphone clock app. You can see it registering various different time zones: London, New York, Beijing. So your smartphone clock can "tell the time" in any of those time zones.

Let's say you do a calculation on your smartphone calculator, and press the = sign. You could easily tell at what local time, in London, New York, Beijing, that = got pressed.

Similarly, say you send a text message. You could easily tell at what local time, in London, New York, Beijing, that <Message Send> got pressed.

It's this |T|ime (the |T| representing lots of different overlapping "times"), which brings what's going on in Θ together. It's how Θ links with what's going on in our bodies.

This is part of what we call |congruence|. Our subjective mind, /S/, is always looking for <coherence>. But |congruence| and <coherence> are not at all the same. They often come into conflict.

The key part of all this is that Theta Θ layer:

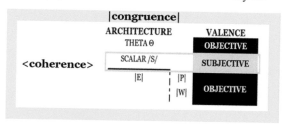

Psychotectics is about re-engineering balance between |congruence| and <coherence>. That's the balance of a cyclist: a dynamic in motion. It can help to think of Θ as being like the stabilisers on the bicycle. They stabilise, because they are linked to the outside world. You can still go where you want to go. But if you try going round a corner in a way which lifts one of the stabilisers off the ground, you will lose balance.

The effect of those stabilisers: that's what we call Autonomic Dynamic Balance ("ADB"). This ADB is related to Biomorphic Autonomic Balance ("BAB"). They are just different way of looking at the self-balancing systems inside the Self.

Our |E|motions point forward in time. That's easier to see, from looking at our thinking.

By contrast, our thoughts react to stimulus, and that stimulus was always in the past. The sun shines on your face. That's happing at a particular moment of |T|ime. It's a few parts of a second later that this stimulus impacts in the brain. Any thoughts we have about sunshine are thoughts looking back at the past.

Our |E|motions are the system that refers the sensory experience of the sunlight to our layer of thoughts. That's why the |E|motions point forward in time.

This is where we get the *car concept* from, that we use in *Matrixial Healing* Recipes. The rear-view mirror is your layer of thinking: always about the past. The headlights are your emotions, looking always forward into the future.

When these functions become confused, as they so often do in dream states, that can cause what we experience as nightmares. *Time Science Therapy* simply helps you to point the rear-view mirror, and the headlights, in the right directions.

By ending the confusion of direction, bad dreams disappear. We use TST in other *Healing* settings as well.

CHAPTER 16

CONGRUENCE INTERFACE THERAPY

Ordinary language really isn't good for talking about these ideas. The words we're used to using bring with them layers of meaning that confuse matters. But let's try this.

Your brain uses two different systems to operate. First, there's a "high level" computer-like system. We call that Theta (symbol Θ). This computer is linked in | T | ime to the outside world: including other Selfs. Unlike an actual computer, this Θ runs "programs", which work with ideas of things which do not exist. You can't get your computer to run code that does not exist. But that's what the Theta Θ brain computer does. The *Matrixial Experiments* have proved this strange truth.

Physically, this Theta Θ brain computer works through the Electromagnetic Cloud, in your brain. Or, we should really say, hovering around your brain bits: those neurons and synapses that you see in magazine articles on the brain. This EM Cloud is as real as the light coming from the red hot filament in your light bulb.

Second there's the thinking/feeling brain. The one that usually comes to mind when we think "brain". All your thoughts, ideas, dreams, wishes: you "Me"-ness. We call that the /S/ubjective continuum, or "layer".

Then there's your physical body |P|. Interacting with senations from the outside world. Interacting with itself. Interacting in very special systems architecture, with your /S/.

That's what this graphic represents:

In Congruence Interface Therapy (CIT), we use *You2* Avatar techniques, to engage Θ<Constructs>. By which we kind of mean computer programs in your EM cloud:

- *CIT Morphonics*: we can use these as Ю|W| interfaces, to change your interaction with the external world, as in improving your writing skills;
- *CIT Holonics*: we can use these to destabilise /S/ <coherence>, as in the Memory *Wipe*;
- we can use them in conjunction with Biomorphics, to effect medicinal interventions.

The capacity for CIT to create interfaces between the Self and the |W|orld is limited only, it seems, by our imagination.

CIT Morphonics
The principles underlying CIT Morphonics have been explained in previous pages.

One way of thinking about this (thought it's not scientifically correct), is that our thoughts and feelings are in a headspace, which is part of a virtual reality spacesuit. By adjusting the settings on the spacesuit, that changes how we create our thoughts and feelings.

Whatever you think and feel in the /S/ layer, is only indirectly connected to the |W|orld. Whenever you deal with the |W|orld, you use Θ<Constructs>: those "computer programs". These connect with the |W|orld by what we label as Ю "interfaces".

These Ю "interfaces" work like putting on 3D glasses. They affect how our |P| body and /S/ mind interact with what they experience as being the world out there.

In CIT Morphonics, we use the connection between your objective mind (Theta Θ) and the objective world. We know how those connections work. They are not connections that depend upon what you're thinking or feeling, from moment to moment.

By communicating from the outside world (the Practitioner) to your objective mind (Theta Θ), we can stimulate that EM cloud to get your subjective brain to act in certain ways. That's not hypnosis: it's the opposite. We need you to be fully awake and aware.

We can also stimulate that EM cloud to create Ю "interfaces". These influence how |P| body and /S/ mind interact with what they experience as the world.

We use the word *Morphonics*, because we are looking at ways that we can adjust the settings on the spacesuit. We use the *You2 Avatar* as a way of getting the Client to connect the /S/ubjective layer of mind, with the "computer program" layer of the spacesuit.

This creates a new dynamic of the |congruence| we have previously been talking about.

That's how *CIT Morphonics* can make immediate changes, so you can (for example):
- write with your other hand
- as a child, improve your writing and reading skills, instantly
- achieve instantly much better co-ordination in sports.

CIT Holonics

What we are doing here, is changing how your /S/ ubjective layer accesses and interprets the Theta Θ "computer program."

The classic case is Memory. We don't have a filing cabinet full of memories, like exhibits in a museum that we go visit with our thoughts. Instead, we re-invent memories, each time we remember.

Memory is not the same as reflex. As these words are being typed, the brain is not "remembering" which letter keys are where, and the relevant instructions from brain to fingers, to find them.

These are reflexes, which means that there's an interface Ю between the Theta Θ EM cloud, and the | W | orld: in this case, they keyboard, and the place it occupies in space and time. Reflex operations are patterns by which the EM cloud stimulates the neurons which operate motor actions.

With a Memory, there is no "out there in the world" connection. Experiences in the world can trigger reflexes, and reflexes can influence our thoughts to create ideas. But, just sitting quietly, or walking along the pavement, and remembering: that's a different system.

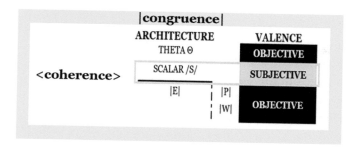

Back to that graphic, our /S/ubjective layer is "looking up" at patterns in the Theta Θ layer. Like looking up at the night sky starfield:

https://www.amazon.co.uk/Pisces-Constellation-Astrology-Horoscope-Journal/dp/1729585345

Our /S/ubjective layer sees whatever it wants to see. It gets into habits of looking at that pattern and saying "Oh yes, that's a fish shape." That process is experienced as Memory.

How we decide to see that night sky starfield can change. It changes all the time. With *CIT Holonics*, we deliberately change how a particular pattern is being viewed. That change our Memory. Instantly and permanently.

This is a really useful and important technique in *Matrixial Healing*. Many problems that we experience are related to Memory-making habits which don't help us. By altering those Memory habits, we can powerfully change how we experience our life.

CHAPTER 17

AVATAR DIALOGUE THERAPY

We use Avatar Dialogue Therapy to bring /S/ back into Autonomic Dynamic Balance.

ADT is about getting you to create Mirrors: which we have designed to reflect back {idents} that attach <Affect>, under the gravitational <coherence> of the Slices. This brings you back to ADB.

As we explained in *I Want To Love But*, this Autonomic Dynamic Balance is inherent in every person ever born. It's simply the manifestation in /S/ of your ASR.

Put simply, a new born baby operates the ASR with very little interference from the immature /S/ continuum. As synaptic connections wire,[30] the /S/ continuum becomes

---

[30] with ultimate synaptic prunings at 7 and in teen years

more populated with {ident} capacity. This increasingly allows us to self-stimulate.

The problem is that we are expert amateurs at self-stimulation. We perpetually alter the Slices Dynamic Balance. In doing that, we interfere with that process by which the ASR seeks to perpetuate Autonomic Dynamic Balance.

Imagine if you were able to influence, by self-stimulation, autonomic functions such as your blood circulation, or blood oxygen supply system. Imagine that, once you started interfering with these autonomic functions, you would have to keep on interfering: trying by manual manipulation to recapitulate that autonomic balance. The result would generally not be favourable to Self-survival.

In ADT:
- rather than getting you to try and think and believe in {thoughts} which are brought to you from "outside";
- we stimulate you to engage with your own <Thoughts>, in {identation} reflection.

A clinical analogy would be to use your own stem cells to rejuvenate mature cells.

ADT is not unique to *Matrixial Therapy*. In Cognitive Behavioural Therapy, there are well-used techniques which involve you "talking to your inner child", and that sort of thing.

We don't find it useful to invent a you from long years ago. Firstly, it's just a creation, kind of like a cartoon, and it's way off being anything like accurate. Secondly, it involves using Memory. It's harmful habits of using Memory that can be involved in so many problems with life. So it's probably not a good idea to drag Memory into trying to make our thinking and feeling clearer.

Looking at the graphic, in ADT we are helping you to create Mirrors, by allowing you to shine a different Light:

Suppose that you're walking down a dark hallway. There are two mirrors that you can see on a wall. You can see them, because there is a light around each mirror:

That's all you can see. These are the only Mirrors that you can bounce your thoughts off:

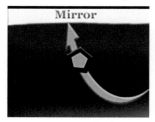

So, you're stuck, and that's how you can come to feel.

With ADT, we simply do this:

We light up another Mirror. It was already there, as part of you: part of your /S/ubjective mind. We just help you to light it up:

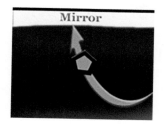 

That can completely change how your thoughts reflect, which changes your interpretation of you and your relationship with the world.

CHAPTER 18

PERSONALITY SLICE THERAPY

We've looked at the 5 Slices of Personality:

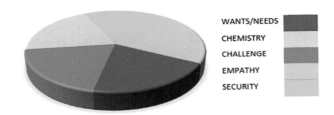

We can see, underlying the different Slices, the momentum of the *ASR* (Anxiety-Soothing Rhythm):

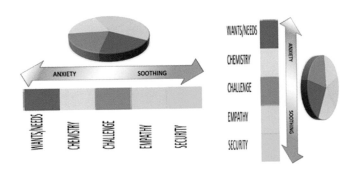

It is our elementary [needs], from birth, that engage the Anxiety reflex. Satisfaction engages our Soothing response: equalised under *Architectural* |congruence|.

With the development of Personality: our thoughts and feelings alter, every moment, the balance between the Slices:

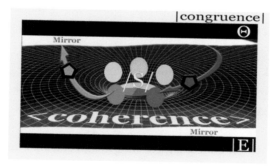

We can trigger our Anxiety, by thinking ideas about our Wants. We can see how Satisfaction signals are part of the Security slice. We have to learn when to start (or accept) a conflict, and when to stop: when matters are Satisfied.

When we are not Satisfied (which is always, after a Satisfaction event has passed), we Need or Want: and the Slices Cycle begins again. The Slices Cycle is how You live your life. Every moment of every day. Your Slices Cycle has been created since your first breath on earth.

It is unique to You, in your personality. Yet that cycle demonstrates both continuity over time (which can be marked by discontinuity) and an averaging into the model Slices.

All of this happens under the "gravitational" force of the /S/ continuum: under our innate need for <coherence>.

Shadow Creation
/S/ is illuminated by mirrors. Reflection is the essential process for doing our thinking in /S/.

We reflect one association of {idents} off another, and so measure their difference or similarity: good/evil; right/ wrong; truth/lies.

We create templates of these {ident} associations, and then use those as reference points. We attach "emotions" to {ident} associations, to make them more powerful. These become our "emotional layers": what we think of as the fundamental elements of our emotional personality.

It's neither easy nor automatic for the 5 Slices to relate in dynamic harmony. All the circumstances of life conspire to de-harmonise, to interfere with the natural "gravity" of our personality.

We can find that the mirroring function doesn't work, or just doesn't seem to work. That perception is probably justified. There's no law of science or nature that says we must be able to understand our life experiences.

We create understandings: and those are more or less efficient to the circumstances of our life. To maintain <coherence> what we all do is create *Shadow Slices (Ш)*.
> *A Shadow Slice Ш is an association of {idents} [ideas] that is unaffected by the dynamics of the Slices.*

Shadow Power

The result is that our <Feelings> and <Thoughts> churn. We feel upset and unbalanced. The Ш sits in our "attic" headspace, as if surrounded by emotional fires and sirens.

Whatever we think and feel, we can't shift the Ш obsession. We are *obsessed*. And possessed by the powerlessness we feel. The process of attaching "emotions" to thoughts is going on perpetually, every moment of the day. But this is not so with Ш.

Ш appear out of our ordinary efforts to acquire {identation} <coherence> in relation to the unfamiliar: to work out what's going on in our life, and why. We manufacture Ш without positively intending to.

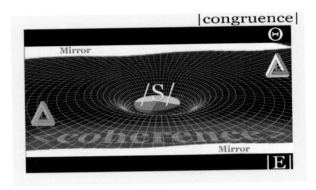

The "impossible triangles" represent ШJ Shadow Slices.

What we then discover is that we can power ШJ by undertaking active suppression of the ASR:

- Our <Anxiety> is going about its usual business.
- But, within /S/, we are deliberately suppressing normal attachment of "emotions" to thoughts.
- So, we are reducing the gravitational force, or size, of the Slices.
- The Mirrors become "starved" of reflective {ident} input, and so output less reflection.
- We thus alter <coherence>.
- <Anxiety> is not reaching Θ<Constructs>.
- Our ШJ gains more relative size.

So, our Objective Behaviour is being altered:

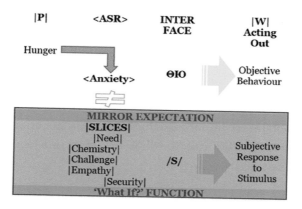

This affects our /S/ ability to {ident} in Mirror Expectation: to undertake the "what if" function. In like manner, it affects our "how, why?" function:

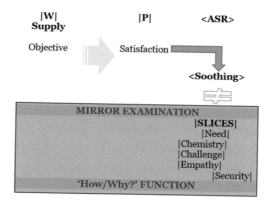

It is commonplace to notice these aspects of Ш, of obsession:

- We become "unidimensional".
- Our ordinary Personality appears to others to become more narrowly focused.
- Emotion and Thought appear disconnected.
- We can appear highly emotional, or emotionally repressed, but the obsession endures.

We obtain an important clue from this commonplace presentation: we can see that Ш act as analogues of Θ<Constructs>.

Removed from the ordinary Slices gravity and Mirror function in /S/, these Ш are trying not to act under equivalence. They are trying to mimic Θ equalisation <Constructs>.
We see all this in the proto-logical madness of obsession.

This is <Me> trying to copy <I>. The Θ<Constructs> in <I> have permanence through | T | ime. Just as Ш pretend to permanence, despite what is going on in and around us. So we see another enduring characteristic of obsession.

We see also another characteristic: the sense that Ш is part of the fabric of "my" being. "I" cannot let that Ш go, without losing myself: or such part of myself as I sense to be the "real" me.

Ш as Obsession
So, we see the dominance characteristics of Ш:

- separated from "emotional" attachment to thoughts
- outside the gravitational force of Slices on {idents}
- stable in isolation
- mimicking Θ<Constructs>
- acting as a version of <I>
- disconnected from the ASR

It's strange that Ш can acquire such seeming dominance in our mind, when they ought to be so fragile. They are disconnected from the ASR: the process which is born into us as our primary survival mechanism, and as our self-teaching system.

These Ш are fragile. That's why we protect them by undermining the normal process in /S/: by suppressing the ASR.

Suppression takes effort. To aid the suppression, we turn to pharmaceuticals and behaviours: processes that can disrupt the ordinary functioning of the ASR.

But that effort takes effort. And we are fighting an ultimately losing battle. We are trying to use artificial measures, to suppress an ASR that is born into us, and which is the electricity for our operating System. No wonder then that suppression of the ASR symptomizes in: lack of energy; listlessness; torpor; depression.

Insomnia is another obvious feature of obsessive Ш.

We cannot allow our guard down. We can't let the ASR go about its usual energetic business in /S/. It takes deliberate effort to suppress the ASR. So we sleep fitfully, with one eye open.

There's the picture of Ш obsession: depressed, unidimensional, pouring energy into distraction, yet insomniac and exhausted. And then we turn to drugs and addictions, to anaesthetise the pain that this awful state brings to us.

Healing Ш Obsession
Understanding these dynamics provides the key to unlocking Ш obsessions: to release suppression of the ASR. We can't:
- think our way out of Ш. If we could, they would simply be normal {idents}, subject to Slices gravity.
- "feel" our way out of Ш, because that's just another flavour of {identation}.

We can't challenge Ш by using our /S/ubjectivity. All that talk therapy which tries to spin effective Ш challenge out of /S/, is not only wasting everyone's time, it tend to make the problem worse:
- The more you look at Ш, the bigger it gets.
- Trying to ignore Ш, makes it bigger too.

This is how we heal Ш obsession: we simply restore ASR function. That's really not difficult. The ASR is the motive energy of your entire Self becoming, and has been since the moment of your birth.

We use *Biomorphic* techniques, to interrupt ASR suppression. It only takes a few moments. Because the ASR is the life of Self. We simple restore your *Biomorphic Autonomic Balance*

We were engineered to perfection. Shadow Slices are helpless when exposed to the force of unsuppressed ASR. Then our Soothing activates. Instead of Shadow, we find balance, peace and power. This allows us to experience that control, which the Shadow never can: despite all its efforts to try.

CHAPTER 19

CLINICAL BOUNDARIES

Everything that we offer in this book is complementary to standard diagnostics and clinical practices of Western medicine. We are not suggesting that you don't use the services of your local or hospital physician.

There are boundaries to what Matrixial Healing offers, especially in this book. If you have an acute illness (cancer, dementia, stroke, heart disease), it's the job of your local and specialist hospital services to provide treatment.

Injuries such as a broken leg, or wound, are also not on our menu of Recipes. *Matrixial Healing* techniques can help with recovery. But when you need a plaster cast or bandaging, that's not something which your mind-body connection can achieve for you.

We find that Western medicine practitioners are intrigued, disinterested, or dismissive, by turns. That's fine. It's how Western medicine has responded to its own innovations over the years. Our job is not to train a BMA registered physician or RCN nurse to change their practice. It's to allow you a wider range of choices in how you deal with things in your own life experience.

Matrixial Healing practitioners learn by doing. It's really just a matter of opening out to the Client and allowing the Client to express what they see as being their problem. A practitioner might, from that self-description, see connections with other issues that can benefit from other Recipes. It's the same in any healing practice.

There are no drugs involved in *Matrixial Healing*. No hypnosis. No altered states. You are always wide-awake. We don't ask for your faith. You don't need to believe in anyone or anything. You can simply experience the Recipe Steps: and see what happens.

It's the natural born power of You, which makes *Matrixial Healing* work. The Recipes simply help you to use that power, as you need it.

CHAPTER 20

THERAPY AND HEALING

Matrixial Therapy is the application of *Matrixial Science*, to human problems. *Matrixial Healing* is the practical application of *Matrixial Therapy*, by invention of Recipes. All of the Recipes have been tested in real life, with real Clients.

As the science develops, that widens the horizons and possibilities for therapy theories. That's all interesting, but the real value of all of it, is in making the lives of real people genuinely better.

The Recipes are standardised. How each Recipe works for each individual, depends on the whole of that individual's life circumstances. That's why we encourage each Client to tell us what they think and feel is their problem. That's the problem which we then address a Recipe to.

The Recipes work like a lock and key system. If you don't have a headache, then the headache Recipe simply won't do anything. It's harmless. It won't hurt you. But it won't achieve anything either.

The point is that your body and your brain do know what's wrong with you. The relevant Recipe simply works to help unlock what they can achieve, working together, without *interference* (however well-intended) from your thoughts and feelings.

The Recipes work best, at least for the first time of using one, with a Practitioner, or even just a friend, to help. As a practical matter, you can't be reading instructions with your eyes closed. It's not easy to learn and remember a set of Steps, then close your eyes and follow them. That's why we created the *Audio Healing Tapes.* Your Steps speaking Practitioner, on demand.

Once you have learned the Steps of a Recipe, then you can practice the Steps yourself. For issues which keep returning, we encourage you to do that. Have a *Matrixial Healing* party: gather some friends and work the Steps with each other.

Have fun realising the power of You. There's nothing better that you can do for your Self.